THE SCIENCE BOOK

First published in 2015 by
Miles Kelly Publishing Ltd
Harding's Barn, Bardfield End Green,
Thaxted, Essex, CM6 3PX, UK

Copyright © Miles Kelly Publishing Ltd 2015

This edition printed 2021

10 9 8 7 6 5 4

Publishing Director Belinda Gallagher
Creative Director Jo Cowan
Managing Editor Amanda Askew
Managing Designer Simon Lee

Senior Editor Claire Philip
Assistant Editors Amy Johnson, Lauren White
Designer Simon Lee
Proofreaders Carly Blake, Fran Bromage
Image Manager Liberty Newton
Production Jennifer Brunwin
Reprographics Stephan Davis
Assets Lorraine King

All rights reserved. No part of this publication
may be reproduced, stored in a retrieval
system, or transmitted by any means,
electronic, mechanical, photocopying,
recording, or otherwise, without the prior
permission of the copyright holder.

ISBN 978-1-78989-025-9

Printed in China

British Library Cataloging-in-Publication Data
A catalog record for this book is available
from the British Library

Made with paper from a sustainable forest

www.mileskelly.net

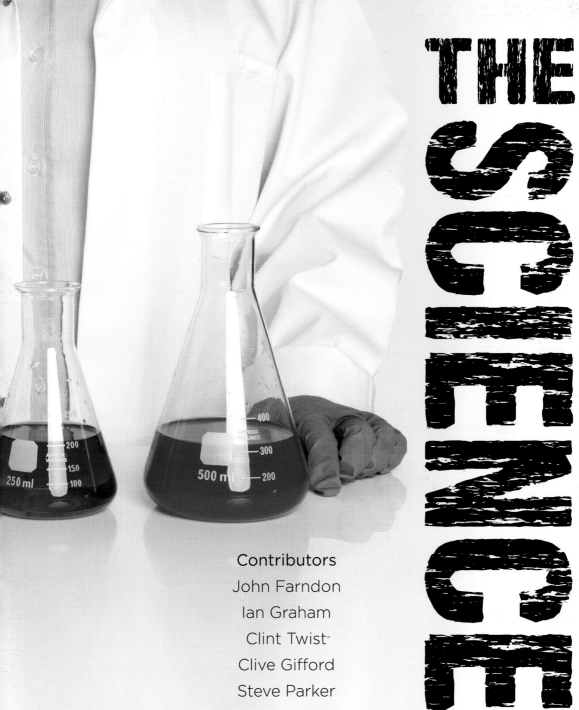

THE SCIENCE BOOK

Contributors

John Farndon

Ian Graham

Clint Twist

Clive Gifford

Steve Parker

Miles Kelly

Contents

Incredible
SCIENCE

Discover the breakthroughs that have shaped the world, and what science can reveal about our remarkable Universe.

◄ The power of a scanning electron microscope (SEM) homes in on the head of a tiny fruit fly, showing the 800 separate lenses that make up each of its two compound eyes.

Big BANGS

Explosions are the most powerful events in the Universe, capable of suddenly blasting apart anything from a rock to an entire giant star. They occur when heat, chemical, or nuclear reactions cause a dramatic and almost instantaneous expansion of gases. Some giant explosions, such as supernovae and volcanoes, occur naturally, but man-made explosions can also be very powerful.

Exploding star

The biggest explosion in the Universe is a supernova—the explosion that ends the life of a supergiant star. It may only be visible for a week, but can be seen far across the Universe, as bright as a galaxy of 100 billion stars.

▼ The Crab Nebula is the remnants of a supernova witnessed by Chinese astronomers in AD 1054.

Blow me down!

To demolish a building without damaging anything nearby, engineers have to make it implode (explode inward). To do this, they place explosive charges in carefully chosen weak points in the building, then set them off in a particular sequence.

▲ Experts need to place explosives very carefully to bring down an unwanted building, such as this 18-story apartment block in Shenyang, China.

Death trap

Land mines are bombs that can be buried just beneath the surface of the ground. Packed with a chemical called Trinitrotoluene (TNT), a land mine explodes by detonation—a powerful shock wave rushes through it, turning all the TNT almost instantly to gas. The gas expands violently, causing terrible damage. A detonator (a tiny explosive device inside the mine) triggers the explosion. Detonators are designed to be triggered when someone steps on the mine or drives a vehicle nearby.

EXPLOSIVE STRENGTH

The power of explosions is often measured in comparison to TNT by weight.

ITEM	POWER
1. Large hand grenade	3 oz (85 g) TNT
2. World War II bomb	6 lb (2.7 kg) TNT
3. "Bunker-buster" bomb	1 ton TNT
4. Hiroshima atom bomb	15 kilotons (15,000 tons) TNT
5. Hydrogen bomb	50 megatons (25 million tons) TNT
6. Mount Toba eruption	85 megatons TNT
7. Supernova	1,000 trillion trillion tons TNT

▶ An entire rock face in a quarry is blasted away by a line of simultaneous explosions.

Volcanic violence

The VEI (Volcanic Explosivity Index) rates the power of explosive volcanic eruptions on a scale from 0 to 8. The Mount St. Helens eruption of 1980 had a VEI of 5. When Mount Toba in Indonesia erupted around 75,000 years ago, it had a VEI of 8, so it was 10,000 times more powerful than Mount St. Helens and was one of the largest explosions on Earth, ever.

▼ Volcanic eruptions are the most powerful natural explosions on Earth.

Rock blast

To blast rock from the ground, quarries usually use dynamite. Invented by Swedish chemist Alfred Nobel (1833–1896), dynamite was the first High Explosive, and consists of sticks of sawdust soaked in nitroglycerin and wrapped in paper. Nitroglycerin contains so much oxygen that it detonates easily when heated. Typically, the heat source is a current of electricity running through a wire set into the dynamite.

Chemical Clash

When a candle burns, metal goes rusty, or a cake rises in the oven, a chemical reaction is taking place. When chemicals meet and react, they change each other to form new chemicals. But not all chemical encounters are quite so gentle.

CHEMICAL REACTIONS ARE CONSTANTLY TAKING PLACE WITHIN THE 100 TRILLION OR SO LIVING CELLS INSIDE YOUR BODY, SO THERE MAY BE MORE THAN 400 BILLION REACTIONS TAKING PLACE INSIDE YOU EVERY SECOND!

Exploding pop

Dropping Mentos mints into cola makes the drink suddenly fizz up in a fountain of froth. The Mentos react chemically with the cola, instantly creating bubbles of carbon dioxide gas, which turn the cola into a gushing foam. Other substances create bubbles in soft drinks, but the chemicals in Mentos make the reaction especially dramatic.

▲ Rusting corrodes tough steel into flaky, brown iron oxide as it reacts with oxygen in the air.

▲ Mentos are covered in minute pits which act as nucleation sites— places that concentrate gas formation.

Acid danger

Strong acids are dangerous chemicals because they react so powerfully. Acids contain hydrogen, and when mixed with water the hydrogen atoms are turned loose as highly reactive "ions." Splashed on skin, acids can cause terrible burns by absorbing water in a reaction that creates a lot of heat. Strong acids can also dissolve metals.

▶ Many spacecraft get off the ground on the back of huge solid-fuel rocket boosters (SRBs)—big tubes packed with enough fuel to get the craft into space. When the fuel is spent, the SRB is jettisoned, and the craft continues its journey with smaller rockets.

Rocket launch

Rockets are blasted into the air by a massive swelling of hot gases created by burning rocket fuel. Burning is a chemical reaction called combustion. When things burn, heat makes fuel combine chemically with oxygen, producing lots more heat. Fires usually draw oxygen from the air, but rocket fuel contains its own oxygen or oxidizer, which is why rockets work in space, where there is no air.

Fireworks

Many fireworks create brilliant flashes of light by burning gunpowder—a mix of charcoal or sugar, potassium nitrate, and sulfur. Charcoal is the fuel, the nitrate gives oxygen, and sulfur keeps the reaction steady. The "bang" is the pop of the paper wrapper around the powder being blown apart by the hot gases.

▼ A firework's colors come from the addition of traces of other chemicals to the mix.

Lithium salts burn **red**

Calcium salts burn **orange**

Copper compounds burn **blue**

Barium compounds burn **green**

A mix of strontium and copper compounds burns **purple**

▶ The reaction of nitric acid with copper creates brown fumes of nitrogen dioxide and green copper nitrate solution.

Dissolving copper

Pouring nitric acid on copper produces a dramatic reaction. The copper dissolves to form a dark, greenish-brown copper nitrate solution, causing brown, poisonous fumes of nitrogen dioxide gas to billow up. Diluting the solution with water will then turn it a clear, azure blue.

Wonder MATERIALS

Natural materials such as diamond and silk can be incredibly tough. But now scientists are creating a range of entirely man-made wonder materials. Some are incredibly light, others are incredibly strong, and some are both.

◀ The high-strength carbon fibers inside CRP help to absorb pressure. In a pole-vaulter's pole, CRP's combination of strength and flexibility gives a vaulter extra lift as it springs straight.

Carbon power

By embedding long fibers made of carbon in plastics, scientists make a material called carbon reinforced plastic (CRP). The plastic keeps it very light, but the fibers give it both strength and flexibility—perfect for the light, strong springiness needed for a pole-vaulter's pole. CRP is known as a "composite" because it combines plastic and carbon.

Jelly light

Aerogels are materials so light that they almost seem to float. Gels are jellylike materials that are mostly liquid. Aerogels are made by sucking liquid out of a gel and replacing it with gas. The gas filling not only makes aerogels amazingly light, but also very good barriers to heat.

CARBON FIBERS ARE FOUR TIMES STRONGER THAN STEEL WHEN PULLED, YET JUST ONE QUARTER OF THE WEIGHT.

▶ Aerogel stops the heat of the bunsen burner flame reaching the flower entirely.

▶ The LCROSS mission smashed a rocket with a wurtzite boron nitride nose into the Moon deliberately to throw up dust for scientists to analyze.

Tough titanium

Alloys are created by adding materials to a metal. Alloys of aluminum and magnesium are tough and light—which is why they are used to build aircraft. But the heat generated as high-speed jets tear through the air may be too much for aluminum alloys. So the fastest jets, such as the *F22 Raptor*, are made mostly from incredibly tough, superlight titanium alloys.

Super strong

Wurtzite boron nitride is the world's hardest material—harder even than diamond. It is used wherever materials need to be really, really tough and cost doesn't matter— from the heads of oil drills to the tips of "bunker-busting" bombs.

▲ With a superlight, superstrong titanium alloy fuselage (main body), the *F22 Raptor* can fly at speeds of up to 1,500 mph (2,400 km/h).

▶ The *Seabreacher* is a submersible made of Kevlar. It is so light and strong that it can burst out of the water like a dolphin.

The toughest threads

In 1961, DuPont chemist Stephanie Kwolek (b. 1923) discovered how to spin fibers from liquid chemicals such as oil. These "aramid" fibers are amazingly strong—threads of the aramid fiber Kevlar are five times stronger than steel. Kevlar has many applications, from helping to make puncture-resistant bicycle tires to strengthening cables used in suspension bridges.

▶ The fibers of Kevlar (a modified form of nylon) are incredibly tough for their weight, so they are used to make stabproof and bulletproof vests.

Deep

Freezing point, when water turns to ice, might seem pretty cold, but it can get much colder in locations such as Siberia and Antarctica. Elsewhere in the Solar System there are places that make Antarctica seem scorching. And in laboratories, scientists can create temperatures so cold that even atoms nearly freeze up.

Maximum chill

The coldest temperature possible is known as Absolute Zero. This is 0 Kelvin, or −459.67°F (−273.15°C). At this temperature atoms have no energy at all and do not even vibrate.

Supercold boomerang

Temperatures near Absolute Zero might only be achieved in a lab, but there is at least one place in the Universe that comes pretty close. In a cloud of gas known as the Boomerang nebula, the temperature is thought to be just 1K (−457.87°F, or −272.15°C).

−273.15°C	−272.15°C
−459.67°F	−457.87°F

Coldest ever

In 2003, scientists cooled sodium gas inside a magnetic container to the coldest temperature ever achieved on Earth. It was just half a nanokelvin— half a billionth of a degree—above Absolute Zero!

MEASURING UP

Temperature is measured on three scales. In everyday life, people use degrees Fahrenheit (°F) or degrees Celsius (°C). You can convert from °F to °C using a simple formula: subtract 32, divide by 9, and multiply by 5. To convert from °C to °F, divide by 5, multiply by 9, and add 32. Scientists may prefer to use the Kelvin scale, which is identical to Celsius but starts at a different place. While 0°C is the freezing point of water, 0K (−459.67°F, or −273.15°C) is the lowest temperature possible and is called Absolute Zero.

Chilled matter

Substances normally exist in one of three states—gas, liquid, or solid—depending on the temperature. But at 17 nanokelvins above Absolute Zero scientists can push gases into another state, known as a Bose-Einstein condensate (BEC). In a BEC, atoms have so little energy that if a beam of light is passed through them then it will come to a complete standstill.

▶ Ultracold rubidium atoms (top) briefly condense into a BEC (center) before evaporating again (bottom).

Inside this flask, helium gas has been cooled to the point where it turns liquid.

▶ Antarctica experiences the coldest natural temperatures on Earth.

Ice station

The coldest outside temperature ever recorded on Earth was −128.6°F (−89.2°C) at the Russian Vostok Station in Antarctica on July 21, 1983.

Helium liquefies

Helium remains a gas until incredibly low temperatures. It finally becomes a liquid at 4K (−452.2°F, or −269°C).

Brrrr!

On February 6, 1933, the temperature in one of the world's coldest towns, Oymyakon, in Siberia, plunged to a bitterly cold −90 °F (−67.7°C).

−269°C	−235°C	−89.2°C	−67.7°C	0°C
−452.2°F	−315°F	−128.6°F	−90°F	32°F

Icy moon

The coldest place in the Solar System is Neptune's moon, Triton. It is so far from the Sun that it receives none of its heat, and temperatures on its surface drop to −315°F (−235°C).

▼ Uniquely, water expands when it freezes, making it less dense, which is why icebergs float.

Neptune

Triton

Freeze!

Water normally freezes solid to become ice at 273.15K (32°F, or 0°C). The addition of salt or pressure keeps it liquid at slightly lower temperatures.

15

Super SCORCH

The more energy things have, the hotter they get. Our bodies get their warmth from the energy released by reacting chemicals. The Sun and stars get their immense heat from the energy released when atoms are forced together by the tremendous pressures in their cores.

▶ Beneath the pale clouds, the surface of Venus is almost hot enough to melt tin.

3 On the boil

A liquid's boiling point is the hottest it can get without becoming a gas. The boiling point of water is normally 212°F (100°C). Beneath geysers, underground pressure allows water to be "superheated" to higher temperatures.

4 Trapped heat

Venus' thick atmosphere traps the Sun's heat, causing temperatures on the planet's surface to reach 896°F (480°C).

37°C	41°C	100°C	480°C	827°C
98.6°F	106°F	212°F	896°F	1,521°F

▲ This thermogram is created using infrared radiation. It indicates differences in temperature by color, from hot (white) to cool (blue).

2 Hot spots

In Dallol, Ethiopia, maximum daily temperatures averaged more than 106°F (41°C) for six years between 1960 and 1966!

5 Hot coals

The temperature of coal fires can vary, but coal can burn at up to 1,521°F (827°C).

1 Body heat

Your body temperature is normally around 98.6°F (37°C), except when you have a fever. Even then it only reaches 104°F (40°C)—much hotter would kill you.

◀ These sulfurous volcanic pools lie in a region that experiences some of the hottest temperatures on Earth: Dallol, in Ethiopia.

6 Molten metal

The bonds between atoms in a metal are very strong, so most metals don't melt until they get very hot. Some steels melt at around 1,517°F (825°C), while tungsten doesn't melt until around 6,170°F (3,410°C).

8 Blue star

The hottest known star in the Universe is Eta Carinae. Its surface reaches more than 72,000°F (40,000°C), which is why it glows blue-hot.

10 Hottest ever

In February 2010, scientists working deep underground in New York, U.S., in the tunnels of the Brookhaven National Laboratory's RHIC (Relativistic Hadron Ion Collider) created the hottest temperatures since the beginning of the Universe. In the RHIC's tunnels, gold atoms smash into each other at almost the speed of light, briefly creating temperatures of 7 trillion°F (4 trillion°C).

▼ In 2005, astronomers realized that superhot Eta Carinae is not one star but two.

3,410°C   5,500°C   40,000°C

6,170°F   9,900°F   72,000°F

The Sun's atmosphere, or corona, reaches a blistering 1,800,000°F (1,000,000°C).

7 Sun burned

The temperature on the surface of the Sun is about 9,900°F (5,500°C). This extreme heat gives sunlight its yellow color—if the Sun were cooler, it would be more reddish. At the center of the Sun, temperatures reach more than 24 million°F (15 million°C)!

9 Big Bang heat

The hottest natural temperature was at the very start of the Universe, during the Big Bang, when temperatures briefly reached 3–5 trillion°F (2–3 trillion°C).

▶ Variations in microwave radiation in this computer map of the sky reveal the lingering glow of the Big Bang.

GIGANTIC Universe

To us tiny humans, Earth seems pretty big. A few centuries ago people thought it was the biggest thing in the Universe. But as telescopes reveal more, it's becoming clear that Earth is seriously small. Some things in space are so huge, they make our entire galaxy seem like a grain of sand on a beach.

Earth

Jupiter

① Biggest planet

At 142,984 km across, Jupiter is the biggest planet in the Solar System. Its diameter is 11.2 times larger than Earth, and its volume is 1.43×10^{15} km³, so you could cram over 1,300 Earths inside Jupiter and still have room to spare!

Earth's diameter is 12,756.1 km. The volume of Earth is 1,083,210 million km³.

Sun

Earth

Jupiter

2 The Sun

The Sun dwarfs Jupiter. It is 1.4 million km across—109 times bigger than Earth. Its volume is $1,412 \times 10^{16}$ km³, which means you could get 1.3 million Earths inside the Sun.

3 Giant star

The giant star Arcturus is 25 times the diameter of the Sun, and is the third brightest star in the night sky.

4 Biggest star

The biggest star we know of is the hypergiant KW Sagitarii. At almost 2 billion km across it is 60 times bigger than Arcturus and more than 1,500 times bigger than the Sun!

LIGHT-YEARS

Dimensions in space are so vast that it's not practical to measure them in kilometers. Instead, astronomers measure things in light-years. Light always travels at the same speed—299,792 km/sec—so distances can be measured by the number of years it takes for light to cross them. A light-year is the distance light travels in a year, which is 9,460 billion km.

Milky Way galaxy

If the Sun were the size of a grain of sand, the Milky Way would be the size of the Sun!

5 Our galaxy

Our Sun is just one of about 400 billion stars in the Milky Way galaxy. The Milky Way is 100,000 light-years across—a million trillion km.

6 Biggest galaxy

The IC 1101 galaxy is 5 million light-years across—50 times as big as the Milky Way.

7 Supercluster

The Milky Way is one of more than 2,000 galaxies in the cluster of galaxies known as the Virgo Cluster. But this cluster is tiny compared with superclusters such as the Perseus-Pisces supercluster, which is more than 300 million light-years across—3,000 times as wide as the Milky Way. If the Sun were the size of a grain of sand, this supercluster would be almost as big as the Solar System.

8 Sloan Great Wall

The Universe is arranged like a gigantic spider's web. All the stars, galaxies, and clusters are concentrated in vast, thin walls. The biggest is the Sloan Great Wall, which is 1.37 billion light-years long—more than 12,000 times as wide as the Milky Way.

Mega IDEAS

As scientists explore the extremes of our world, they often need to use huge, complex pieces of equipment. Exploring the vastness of the Universe requires massive telescopes and research stations in space. Strangely, some of the biggest and most elaborate machines have been built to study things that are so tiny, they are invisible to the naked eye.

A remote-controlled arm is used to move equipment and astronauts

There is always at least one Russian Soyuz spacecraft docked at the ISS as a lifeboat in case of an emergency, such as crew illness

Visiting spacecraft join the ISS at docking points

Solar panels swivel as the ISS orbits so they point at the Sun

International Space Station

The biggest space station ever built, the ISS orbits between 173 mi (278 km) and 286 mi (460 km) above Earth. It is so big, it can be seen from the ground with the naked eye. Its parts were carried up bit by bit by dozens of space flights, then assembled in space by astronauts in more than 130 separate space walks.

▲ The ISS hurtles around Earth at an average speed of 17,239.2 mph (27,743.8 km/h), completing 15.7 orbits per day.

Human Genome Project

Every cell in your body carries instructions to keep you alive (and create your children), all contained on a tiny string of the chemical DNA. The instructions are in the form of thousands of chemical sequences called genes. The Human Genome Project was a huge international program to map the human genome (identify exactly where on human DNA every single gene occurs). The project began in 1990 and was completed in 2003.

▲ A computer image shows a tiny part of the map of DNA, with each bar showing one of the four chemical bases that make up the code.

Very Large Array

Radio waves are very long, so capturing radio signals from distant stars and galaxies effectively requires huge radio dishes. Instead of a single big dish, they can use an array (series) of linked dishes spread over a vast area. The Very Large Array (VLA) on the Plains of San Augustin, New Mexico, U.S., has 27 dishes arranged in a "Y" shape up to 22 mi (36 km) apart.

Millennium Run

The Millennium Run is one of the biggest computer simulations ever created. The idea behind it was to create a computer model of every particle in a section of the Universe to test theories on how the Universe developed. In 2005 the first run traced what happened to every single one of ten billion particles, involving 20 million galaxies in a region of space 2 billion light-years across. Images generated by the simulation show how dark matter—a form of matter that cannot be detected by telescopes as it does not emit any radiation—is distributed across the Universe.

▼ A computer image generated by the Millennium Run shows how dark matter is distributed in the local Universe—an area 206 million light-years in distance across.

▲ Each of the 27 dishes in the VLA measures 82 ft (25 m) across.

RADIO TELESCOPES SUCH AS THE VLA HAVE MAPPED CLOUDS OF GAS SHOWING THE SHAPE OF THE MILKY WAY, AND DISCOVERED WHAT SEEMS TO BE A MASSIVE BLACK HOLE AT ITS CENTER.

Small WORLD

Looking at your skin through a magnifying glass reveals all kinds of details invisible to the unaided eye. However, scientists have now developed microscopes that allow us to see a world that is on a much smaller scale. Even a good magnifying glass only magnifies objects by a few times. The most powerful scanning tunneling microscopes (STMs) magnify things billions of times, and can reveal particles smaller than atoms.

Pepper

Salt

1 Salt and pepper

10^{-3} m (1 mm)

To the unaided eye, pepper looks pretty much like salt, only dark brown. But a good light microscope shows just how different they are. Pepper is, of course, the seed of a plant. Salt is a mineral crystal.

2 Human hair

10^{-4} m (100 micron)

Your hair may feel pretty smooth and fine, but under a microscope you can see that each hair has a rough surface, and looks rather like a tiny tree trunk.

3 Red blood cells

10^{-5} m (10 microns)

The most powerful light microscopes can show the tiny red cells in blood, but to see their shapes clearly you need a scanning electron microscope (SEM). SEM pictures show that when red blood cells are healthy, they are a neat button shape.

4 Bacteria

10⁻⁶ m (1 micron)
You can just about see bacteria with light microscopes, but SEM pictures can show detailed close-ups.

◀ Bacteria such as *Helicobacter pylori* live in many human stomachs, and can cause stomach upsets.

5 Virus

10⁻⁷ m (100 nanometers)
Viruses are much tinier than bacteria and can only be seen with electron microscopes, such as the transmission electron microscope (TEM).

Coronaviruses cause anything from colds to gastric illnesses. They got their name because they look like crowns through an electron microscope.

SCIENTISTS CAN MAKE ELECTRONIC DEVICES AS SMALL AS A SINGLE ATOM. VERY SOON, A POWERFUL COMPUTER NEED BE NO BIGGER THAN A GRAIN OF SAND.

6 Molecule

10⁻⁸ m (10 nanometers)
Atomic force microscopes (AFMs) and the most powerful TEMs can show actual strands of DNA.

◀ DNA can be seen clearly with a TEM, magnified almost half a million times.

7 Atom

10⁻⁹ m (1 nanometer)
To see an atom, you need a scanning tunneling microscope (STM).

MICROSCOPES

Light or optical microscopes use combinations of lenses to magnify things. They can magnify up to about 2,000 times. The smallest thing they can see is about 500 nanometers (500 billionths of a meter).

Electron microscopes can show things up to 20,000 times smaller. They don't use lenses at all—they fire electrons at their subjects and record the way the electrons bounce off. Instead of seeing an object directly, you look at a picture of it that builds up on a screen.

Scanning tunneling microscopes (STMs) and atomic force microscopes (AFMs) work by touch. AFMs run a sharp point that looks similar to an old-fashioned record needle over the subject. These microscopes can show atoms.

Microscopic

Zoo

In recent years, scanning electron and tunneling microscopes have homed in on the world of insects and microbes to reveal them in amazing detail and clarity. Even the tiniest bugs appear as large and monstrous as creatures from another world. There are many, many more different species of these microscopic organisms than there are in all the rest of the living world put together.

◄▲ A tiny fruit fly seen through an SEM with a close-up of the "talons" on its leg (inset left).

Small fly

Magnified more than 800 times, this SEM image shows the two birdlike talons on the end of a fruit fly's leg. The hairlike stalks beneath the talons are covered with adhesive pads or "pulvilli." These allow the fruit fly to cling to vertical surfaces such as glass, which appear completely smooth to the naked eye. Scientists are hoping to develop artificial nanomaterials that adhere in a similar way.

Stomach bug

Transmission electron microscopes (TEMs) reveal the microscopic zoo living inside the human stomach. This is the bacteria *Helicobacter pylori* magnified 7,700 times. These bacteria get their name, "pylori," from the fact that they live in the pyloric (lower) part of many people's stomachs. Fortunately, they usually have no effect.

▲ *Helicobacter pylori* can move around by whipping its tail or "flagella."

Living jewels

Diatoms are algae that float in water and get their energy from the Sun, like plants do. They are so small, they can only be seen properly with an SEM. But SEMs reveal them to be astonishingly beautiful geometric "jewels." There are more than 100,000 different species.

▶ The spiny surfaces of these minute pollen grains help them stick to feathers and fur.

Plant packet

SEMs reveal the huge variety of different forms of pollen. Pollen is the dusty substance that flowers spread to help them reproduce. Each grain is a tough case holding male sex cells that must be delivered to the female ova or egg to create a seed for a new flower. Grains are so tough, they last tens of thousands of years, so archeologists can use SEM pictures of ancient pollen to identify plants that were growing long ago.

▼ A magnified head louse appears monstrous as it climbs along a human hair.

MICROSCOPIC NEMATODE WORMS MAKE UP 90 PERCENT OF ALL LIFE ON THE OCEAN FLOOR.

High life

In close-up, a head louse clinging to a human hair looks like a monster crawling along a tightrope. Head lice are tiny, wingless insects that live in the hair of living humans, lay their eggs on hair shafts, and feed entirely on human blood, sucked from the scalp.

▲ These fantastic, beadlike diatoms are only one hundredth of the width of a human hair.

▼ Protozoa such as this amoeba may be microscopic, but they are animals that can move around of their own accord.

The smallest animals

Protozoa are the smallest of all animals, made from just one cell. Most can only be seen under a microscope, yet they breathe, move, and reproduce like bigger animals. They live in water or damp places. Some protozoa can cause serious diseases. Others are helpful because they eat harmful bacteria and are food for fish and other animals.

Light FANTASTIC

I n the last 50 years, scientists have come to understand light and radiation so well that they can now do things with it that might once have seemed like magic. The most exciting effects, such as the creation of holograms and measurements of astonishing accuracy, are achieved with laser light, but other kinds of light can be used for anything from seeing a living brain in action to spotting an invisible thumbprint at a crime scene.

◄ A magnetic resonance image (MRI) scan "sees" inside a living body, showing both skeleton (white) and lungs (orange) in 3-D.

Body scan

Doctors and scientists use magnetic resonance imaging to take 3-D pictures that show the inside of the human body. It works by using powerful magnets to draw the nuclei (centers) of all the body's atoms into alignment. The magnet is then switched off. As the nuclei twist back to their normal position, they send out photons (particles of radiation). Detectors pick up the photons and a computer can then build up the 3-D image.

▼ This hologram shows Lindow man, a body preserved for 2,000 years in an English marsh.

Hologram magic

Holograms are 3-D images made by splitting a laser beam in two. One half, the reference beam, goes to the camera. The other bounces off the subject, breaking up the neat pattern of laser light waves. The camera records how this broken pattern interferes with (differs from) the reference beam, and this data can be used to project a 3-D image using lasers.

Nonmoving holograms have been around for half a century, but scientists are developing solid-looking moving holograms. In time, they may be able to create holograms that look like the real object.

▼ Ultraviolet (UV) light shows up otherwise invisible traces of blood and other body fluids splashed on a wall at a crime scene.

The first laser beams were created in 1960 by Theodor Maimann. Laser light is like no natural light in the Universe. All natural light is said to be "incoherent" because it is a chaotic mix of lots of photons (particles of light) of different wavelengths. In laser light, the photons are all identical and in sync. The result is an intense beam of light of just one color, which is much harder to scatter than ordinary light. In fact, laser light can be bounced off the Moon and back and still stay in a single, tight beam.

Spotting the crime

Criminals may think they've left no trace of their crime, but ultraviolet (UV) light can reveal all kinds of invisible evidence. Fingerprints and traces of body fluids at the crime scene that cannot otherwise be seen show up clearly under UV—light made of waves slightly shorter than violet light, just too short to be visible.

Making stars

Shifting dust in the air makes it hard to get a clear view of space beyond. That's why stars appear to twinkle. Astronomers use computers to adjust telescope images for the dust, using bright stars as a reference—a technique known as Adaptive Optics (AO). But there aren't always bright stars in the part of the sky astronomers need to study, so instead they create their own guide star using a laser. As the laser is shone up into the sky it creates a little "star" where it hits sodium gas and makes it glow.

◄ An observatory sends out a beam of laser light to create a sodium laser guide star in the sky for astronomers.

Laser precision

The precision of a laser beam means it can be used to take incredibly accurate measurements. For example, geologists can bounce lasers off satellites to measure the distance between continents an ocean apart to within a few millimeters. LiDAR (Light Detection and Rangefinding) is an amazing way of building up an instant 3-D map, in which a survey plane or satellite moves over a target and scans it with pulses of laser light. Detectors then pick up the reflections and use them to build up a 3-D image.

Extreme Conditions

Some scientists learn about the world in laboratories, but others venture into the most extreme conditions to gather data and make observations. To find out more, some scientists will fly into the heart of a hurricane, endure months in the bitter chill of the Antarctic, walk into an active volcano, crawl into deep caves, dive to the depths of the ocean, climb towering rain forest trees, and much more. Where there is something to be learned, scientists will go.

Hot and hazardous

Volcanoes are incredibly dangerous up close. Although a protective suit provides a shield against the heat and fumes, it will not save a person in the event of an eruption. The two most famous volcanologists (volcano experts) of all time, Maurice and Katya Krafft, were killed, along with 41 journalists, when they were filming on Japan's Mount Unzen in 1991. Without warning, the volcano blasted out an avalanche of searingly hot gas and ashes that engulfed them in seconds.

Volcanologists test material from a live volcano.

DANGEROUS DINNERS

Cooking in chemist Helen Maynard-Casely's kitchen is a dangerous business. She uses ordinary ingredients such as cream, sugar, and bread, but she subjects them to extreme pressures and temperatures to see what happens to them. She might chill cream with liquid nitrogen at –274°F (–170°C), or squeeze burnt toast hard enough to turn the carbon it contains into diamonds. Her colleague, Colin Pulham, at the Edinburgh Centre for Science Under Extreme Conditions, in Scotland, makes diamonds by blasting carbon with dynamite!

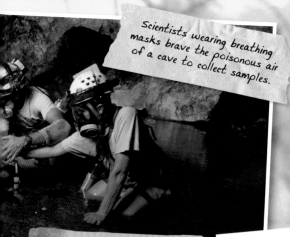

Scientists wearing breathing masks brave the poisonous air of a cave to collect samples.

Storm chasers

Tornadoes are incredibly powerful storms. Their twisting funnels of winds can blast a building apart or whip a truck into the air. But they are localized and very brief, rarely lasting more than 15 minutes. Scientists such as Chuck Doswell and Dr. Josh Wurman have to chase the tornadoes they study at high speeds—and risk being caught in the storm themselves. The chase is so exciting that many people now pursue tornadoes just for the thrill, but authorities fear someone may soon be killed.

Going underground

Professor Hazel Barton is willing to go into Earth's depths to pursue her studies of bacteria that live in extreme conditions. Bacteria such as these can only be found in the most inaccessible caves. To study them, Professor Barton has to squeeze through narrow passages and swim through underwater lakes where visibility is practically zero and the air is often poisonous.

A storm chaser hurriedly sets down a weather probe in the path of an oncoming tornado.

The probe will measure conditions right in the heart of the tornado.

This tiny hammerhead shark being studied by a marine biologist is harmless, but it has much bigger, more ferocious relatives.

Ocean peril

Exploring the ocean can be difficult and even life threatening. In the surface waters, there is not only the danger of drowning, but also the threat of serious injury from potentially lethal creatures such as sharks, jellyfish, and stonefish. Deeper down, the water is bone-chillingly cold and pitch-dark—and the pressure is enough to crush a car.

Feel the FORCE

Force is what makes things happen. It can push things or pull them, speed them up or slow them down, draw them together or split them apart. Without forces, nothing would start or stop. Some forces—such as the force required to move your eye across this page—are tiny, while others are incredibly strong. Machines give us much more force than our bodies are capable of alone, but the most extreme forces are natural.

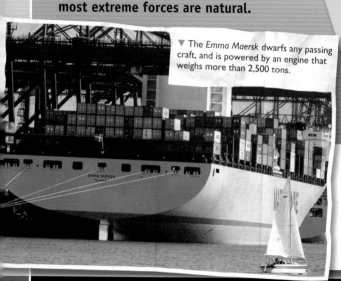

▼ The *Emma Maersk* dwarfs any passing craft, and is powered by an engine that weighs more than 2,500 tons.

Muscle cars

Power is a measure of not only force but also how fast it is delivered. A kilowatt (kW) of power is a force of one newton delivered at one meter every second. A small family car can get by with less than 50 kW of power, but to accelerate quickly, high-performance cars need a lot of force, very fast. That's why the *SSC Ultimate Aero TT*'s engine generates an incredible 960 kW of power.

Ship power

The more weight that must be moved, the more force you need, so the world's most powerful motors are on the world's heaviest ship—the *Emma Maersk*, which is driven through the ocean by the mighty Wärtsilä-Sulzer RTA96 diesel. It produces more than 83 megawatts (million watts) of power—as much as 10,000 high-performance cars!

MEASURING FORCE

One newton is the force that makes a mass of one kilogram accelerate at one meter per second every second. It's roughly equivalent to the force you'd use if you threw a big pebble into the sea.

45 N	The force required to push an adult over
670 N	The force of a karate chop breaking a plank
300–730 N	The gravitational force holding you on the planet
2,000 N	A good kick on a football
2,900 N	The force of a karate chop breaking a concrete slab
7,000 N	The force of an accelerating car
500,000 N	The force of a large locomotive
770,000 N	The thrust of a jumbo jet's engines
33,000,000 N	The thrust of the *Saturn V* rocket
200 million trillion N	The gravitational pull between the Moon and the Earth
350 billion trillion N	The gravitational pull between the Sun and the Earth

ONE OF THE STRONGEST FORCES EVER MADE BY HUMANS WAS FOR THE SATURN V ROCKET THAT LAUNCHED THE APOLLO SPACECRAFT TO THE MOON. THE FIRST STAGE OF THE ROCKET GENERATED A THRUST OF 3.4 MILLION N.

STOP

▼ The *SSC Ultimate Aero TT* is the most powerful sports car ever, and can reach a speed of more than 270 mph (430 km/h).

Fundamental forces

There are many kinds of force. "Contact" forces directly push or pull, for example when someone hits a ball. Others act "at a distance," with no direct contact. All the fundamental forces of the Universe—gravity, electromagnetism, and the two nuclear forces that hold atoms together—act at a distance. Forces like this depend inversely on the distance between the affected objects—that is, they get weaker the further apart they are.

Star quake

There are forces in the Universe that make anything on Earth look minuscule. On December 27, 2004, a flash of energy burst from the star SGR 1806-20 in what is called a "star quake." This quake had a power of 10,000 trillion trillion trillion watts. If the star had been even 10 light-years away from Earth it would have shaken the Earth to bits. Luckily, it was much further away!

▲ The energy burst from the star SGR 1806-20 in 2004 was so huge, it was visible from Earth.

◄ Buildings were sent crashing down by the San Francisco quake of 1989.

MOUNTAIN SHAKING

Even the thrust of a rocket such as the mighty *Saturn V* is dwarfed by the natural forces involved in earthquakes. The faintest tremor has 60 million watts of power, while the most powerful earthquake ever, which hit Chile in 1960, generated 11 million billion watts. With this kind of force, earthquakes can lift up and knock down entire mountains.

STRANGE
Brains

Most scientists are sensible, rational people, but sometimes they are working on ideas too complictated for most regular people to understand, so they can come across as being a bit peculiar. A few scientists become so obsessed with their research that their behavior seems truly eccentric (to put it mildly). Here are a few of the strangest scientists ever.

ELIXIR OF LIFE

The German alchemist, physician, and theologian Johann Konrad Dippel (1673–1734) was convinced he could find an elixir that would give people eternal life—and bring dead people back to life. He lived in Castle Frankenstein in Germany and tales of his experiments with corpses inspired Mary Shelley's famous story of Doctor Frankenstein and his monster. Dippel also invented Prussian Blue, the first of the chemical dyes that are used to give most clothes their colors today.

▲ Johann Dippel thought he could find a liquid that would bring the dead back to life.

He's electric

Serbian-born American Nikola Tesla (1856–1943) was the genius who gave us our modern electricity supply by pioneering the use of Alternating Current (AC) to send power over huge distances. However, some of Tesla's theories were slightly more eccentric. His idea of transmitting energy through the air without wires is now becoming a reality, but thankfully his plans for a giant death ray have not come to fruition.

▶ Nikola Tesla's many unusual ideas included using magnetic coils to turn Earth into a huge steerable spaceship.

I CAN FLY!

Some of the bravest—or craziest—scientists have been those who attempted to fly. There are many who tried strapping on wings to jump from high places and never lived to tell the tale. One of the most daring and successful was German flier Otto Lilienthal (1848–1896). Lilienthal made more than 2,000 pioneering hang glider flights in the 1890s. Sadly, a flight in 1896 proved fatal, but his experiments were crucial to the Wright brothers' famous first plane flight seven years later in 1903.

▶ Otto Lilienthal in 1893 on one of his glider flights in the hills near Berlin, Germany.

▶ Kevin Warwick shows off the cyborg arm that responds to his thoughts.

The cyborg

Cyborgs are creatures of science fiction—they are half-human and half-robot. But British scientist Kevin Warwick (b. 1954) is turning himself into a cyborg for real. He isn't mad, though—he wants to experiment on himself to find ways of helping disabled people. He has implanted electronic devices into his arm that link his nervous system directly to a computer, so that he can operate the computer just by thinking.

ROCKET MAN

One of the pioneers of space technology, German-born American engineer Wernher von Braun (1912–1977) was obsessed with rockets from a very young age. Aged 12, von Braun packed his toy wagon with firecrackers and lit them, causing him to shoot across the street while his neighbors looked on in horror. The incident resulted in him being arrested by the police. However, von Braun was not so much mad as just dedicated to his science.

▶ Wernher von Braun was responsible for the development of the V2 rocket in Germany, and went on to become a leading figure in the American space program after World War II.

BLACK Hole

Black holes are places where gravity is so strong that it sucks everything in, including light. They form when a star or part of a galaxy gets so dense that it collapses under its own gravity, shrinking to an infinitely small point called a singularity. Gravity around the singularity is so ferocious that it sucks in light, space, and even time.

WE CAN'T STUDY THE POINT AT WHICH LIGHT DISAPPEARS IN A BLACK HOLE IN SPACE, BUT SCIENTISTS AT THE UNIVERSITY OF ST. ANDREWS, SCOTLAND, CREATED A VIRTUAL BLACK HOLE IN THE LABORATORY USING PULSES OF LASER LIGHT.

Old supernova

Some black holes form when an old giant star collapses into a supernova. Astronomers can't actually see black holes, but sometimes they can detect their presence from their effect on other objects. Stars often form pairs, or binaries. If one star is a black hole, astronomers might be able to see the effect of its gravity on the visible companion star. They may also spot X-rays bursting from matter ripped off the companion star by the power of the black hole.

▶ An artist's impression of a black hole (right) ripping matter off its companion star (left) in a binary pair.

Supermassive

In the center of the Milky Way, in a region called Sagittarius A*, 20 million stars are packed into a space just 3 light-years across, and hurtling round at incredible speeds. Calculations show they must be in the grip of the gravity of an object two to three million times as heavy as the Sun yet only twice as big. It must be what astronomers call a "supermassive black hole." There is thought to be one at the heart of every spiral-shaped galaxy.

▲ Astronomers think the pink cloud near the galaxy NGC 4438 may be a bubble of gas belched out by a supermassive black hole at the galaxy's center. NGC 4438 is one of a pair of galaxies known as the Eyes Galaxies.

▲ The powerful magnetic forces created by a black hole inside the galaxy Pictor A shoot out an X-ray jet thousands of light-years long.

Jet propulsion

Black holes don't just suck things in. As they mash up the matter they draw in, they can spew out giant jets of the remnants—electrons and other subatomic particles. The gigantic black hole at the heart of the M87 galaxy is shooting out an astonishingly brilliant beam of these remnants for thousands of light-years into the darkness, like some kind of galactic searchlight.

INSIDE A BLACK HOLE

In every black hole there is a point of no return, called the event horizon. Beyond this point, time has no meaning and not even light can get out.

If you saw someone falling into a black hole, you would never see them reaching the event horizon. Instead, you would see them going slower and slower and getting redder and dimmer until they finally faded away altogether.

If you fell into a black hole, you would be stretched out like spaghetti because the pull of gravity on your feet would be so much stronger than on your head. Astronomers believe you'd become so "spaghettified" that you would eventually be ripped apart.

As you are being ripped apart, time would speed up dramatically—you'd see the future flashing by outside the black hole. But you couldn't get out, or get a message out, since even light cannot escape a black hole.

Tunnel through time

Some scientists think black holes may be linked to white holes. White holes, if they exist, would be the opposite of black holes—places where matter and radiation spew out into space like a fountain. A few scientists think that black holes and white holes could be linked by a tunnel through space and time called a wormhole. If there are such things as wormholes, it might be possible to slip through them to travel vast distances through space instantly, or even to travel through time to the future or the past.

A MASSIVE Mystery

▼ The LHC has to run at incredibly low temperatures. This is the refrigeration or cryogenics unit.

Deep beneath the countryside on the border of Switzerland and France is a circular tunnel more than 16 mi (27 km) long. Inside it is the world's largest machine—the Large Hadron Collider (LHC). It is basically a long, ring-shaped tube in which hadrons (subatomic particles) are accelerated round and round, reaching incredible speeds, and then smashing together. What scientists hope to see in the smashed bits may answer fundamental questions about the Universe, such as why things have mass, momentum, and inertia.

▶ This computer simulation of the detector screen in the LHC shows what may happen if a Higgs boson (see far right) is found, sending out a spray of subatomic particles as it breaks up.

◀ The LHC uses powerful magnets to accelerate particles through a tube in opposite directions at high speeds and then smash them together head-on. Special sensors track the new particles created briefly as the smashed particles break up.

A crash test shows the effects of momentum dramatically—the car starts to crumple just before the test dummy is catapulted forward.

THE SEARCH FOR THE HIGGS BOSON

Forces such as electromagnetic radiation are transmitted by tiny "messenger" particles known as bosons. But scientists don't really know what mass is, or why things have inertia and momentum. It may all be down to a particle called the Higgs boson. This is how it might work:

Imagine a celebrity arriving at a party. As she swans in, fans (the Higgs bosons) crowd round her, giving her mass. The crowd makes it hard to get her moving, so she has inertia, but once they all start moving it's hard to stop them, so they give her momentum, too.

The mysterious Higgs boson is one of the things scientists are hoping to see among the smashed bits of particles in the LHC.

Momentum

Once an object is moving, it won't stop unless forced to because its mass propels it on. This is called momentum. It's what keeps the planets orbiting the Sun, and what carries a speeding roller coaster up the next incline. There's no more convincing demonstration of momentum in action than a crash test. When the test car slams into a wall, the momentum of the car and the dummy try to carry them on, which is why they smash into the wall with such force.

◄ In order to throw the heavy shot, the shot-putter has to overcome all its inertia.

Inertia

It takes force to get something moving, because an object's mass keeps it rooted to the spot. This is called inertia. That's why a shot-putter has to be so strong to get the heavy shot moving.

Mass

Momentum and inertia both depend on mass—the amount of matter involved. The heavier something is (the more massive it is), the more momentum and inertia it has.

Energy UNLEASHED

The nucleus of most atoms is fairly stable—but not always. Sometimes nuclei can partly disintegrate (radioactivity) or split in two (nuclear fission). Under severe pressure, different nuclei may fuse together (nuclear fusion). When any of these things happen, it unleashes matter and energy, known as radiation. The Universe is filled with natural radiation, and it's the energy of nuclear fusion that makes stars shine. Humans have learned to harness this energy, both to generate power and to create nuclear bombs—the most devastatingly powerful weapons of all time.

Solar power

The Sun shines because it is so big that the pressure in its core is huge—enough to force the nuclei of hydrogen atoms to fuse to make helium. The energy released by each individual fusion may be tiny, but there are so many atoms involved that the heat generated is enormous. This nuclear fusion drives temperatures in the Sun's core to 27 million°F (15 million°C) and makes the surface glow white-hot.

RADIOACTIVITY

The nucleus of an atom is made of two kinds of particle—protons and neutrons—and there are three main kinds of radioactivity:

Alpha decay is when an alpha particle (two neutrons and two protons) breaks away from the nucleus.

Beta decay is when a neutron splits to form a proton, emitting a beta particle (an electron) and a particle called an antineutrino.

Gamma rays are not emitted from the nucleus, but are a kind of electromagnetic radiation emitted from electrons like light, but they are very energetic and dangerous.

NUCLEAR FISSION

Conventional fuel is too bulky for submarines to carry for long voyages underwater, so many big subs are now powered by nuclear reactors. The reactors generate heat from the fission (splitting) of uranium atoms, which are large and easily split. The heat creates steam to drive the submarine's turbines. Just a few small rods of uranium fuel power a sub for many long voyages.

◄ Nuclear power allows submarines to stay on patrol underwater for long periods.

▼ Radiocarbon dating has helped scientists work out that Tollund man, whose preserved remains were found in a Danish bog, dates back to the 4th century BC.

THE BIGGEST BOMB EVER EXPLODED WAS THE 50 MEGATON RUSSIAN H-BOMB KNOWN AS THE TSAR BOMBA, WHICH WAS DETONATED IN OCTOBER 1961 IN NOVA ZEMLAYA, EASTERN SIBERIA.

Carbon dating

Some variations of atoms, called isotopes, are more likely to disintegrate radioactively than others. The radioisotope carbon-14, for example, is present in all living things, but when they die, the isotopes begin to disintegrate. The rate of disintegration is so steady that by measuring the proportion of carbon-14 isotopes left in remains of once living things, scientists can tell exactly how long they have been dead. This process is called radiocarbon dating and it is one of the most valuable archeological techniques.

▶ Thermonuclear bombs use a small fission bomb to set off a massive hydrogen fusion bomb. It starts with a gigantic fireball, such as this one in a test in the Pacific in 1958.

H-bomb

The nuclear bomb that destroyed Hiroshima in Japan in 1945 depended on the fission of big atoms such as uranium and plutonium. But even more terrible bombs were created by the fusion of tiny hydrogen atoms. The hydrogen was encased in a small bomb that was exploded first to create the pressure to fuse the hydrogen atoms. These hydrogen or H-bombs are now known as thermonuclear weapons.

Radiation danger

Exposure to radiation can be very dangerous. Gamma radiation is the most dangerous because the particles are small enough to penetrate the skin. The larger particles of alpha and beta radiation are less immediately dangerous, but if you eat any food containing them, they can also cause illnesses from nausea to cancer, and may even result in death.

◀ The accident at the Chernobyl Nuclear Plant, Ukraine, in 1986 was one of the worst ever, releasing radiation that was carried by wind far across Europe. The red color in this satellite image of the area around the nuclear plant indicates radioactivity.

Birth of the
UNIVERSE

	10^{27} °C	10^{12} °C
	10^{-32} sec	3 min

0 seconds
First the Universe was a tiny hot ball that grew as big as a football, then cooled to (just) 10 billion billion billion°C.

10^{-43} seconds
In the "Planck" era, the four basic forces (gravity, electromagnetism, and the two nuclear forces) were joined as a single force.

10^{-12} seconds
The Universe became a sea of particles such as quarks and gluons, which began to gain mass.

10^{-32} seconds
The forces split into four and space swelled quadrillions of times in less than a fraction of a second, from something smaller than an atom to bigger than a galaxy. This is known as inflation.

3–20 minutes
Gravity and the other forces began to pull things together. Quarks and gluons joined to form the nuclei of the smallest atoms, hydrogen. Then hydrogen nuclei joined to make helium nuclei.

300,000 years
The first atoms formed and made gases.

One million year
After one million years or so, the gases began to curdle like sour milk into long strands called filament with vast dark holes called voids in between.

alaxies are flying out and away from each other in all directions. This means the Universe must be expanding rapidly, so in the past it must have been much smaller. Indeed, it is now thought that long ago—about 13.5 billion years ago—the Universe was tinier than an atom. That was when it burst into being in what is often called the Big Bang. After the Big Bang, the Universe began swelling with such force and speed that astronomers are not sure if it will ever stop.

2,726 °C	253.15 °C	−270 °C
00,000 years	1 billion years	Today (13.7 billion years)

SCIENTISTS HAVE WORKED OUT THAT THE BIG BANG WAS ACTUALLY MORE LIKE A DEEP HUM OR THE ROAR OF A JET PLANE THAN A BANG.

OLD AND YOUNG
When astronomers observe galaxies 13 billion light-years away, it is as if they are staring into ancient history. But the galaxies they are seeing are (relatively) very young. The oldest stars we can see are quite close to us, in globular clusters, which are groups of a few million stars within the Milky Way. Stars in the NGC 6397 cluster are 13.4 billion years old.

Today
The Sun is almost halfway through its life today, but new stars and planets are forming all the time throughout the Universe.

4.567 billion years
The Solar System was born— the Earth and other planets were formed from a ring of dust around the Sun.

0.5–1 billion years
The filaments gradually clumped into clouds. Eventually, these clouds formed stars and galaxies.

Body SCIENCE

Take a top-to-toe tour of the human anatomy, from amazing microscopic views to X-rays of the body in action.

◀ A scanning electron microscope (SEM) reveals a clot of red and white blood cells in a blood vessel.

Building
THE BODY

The body is made up of 12 different, interlinking systems—each one performs a particular task, but they are all dependent on each other. Some, such as the circulatory system, spread throughout the body. Others, such as the digestive system, are mainly in one place.

4

INNARDS

1
The **digestive system** breaks down food into chemicals that the body can absorb and use for fuel and materials, and then removes the rest as waste. It includes the stomach, intestines, and anus.

2
The **urinary system** removes excess water as urine. It also gets rid of impurities in the blood. It includes the kidneys and bladder.

3
The **reproductive system** consists of the sex organs that enable humans to have children. Males have a penis, scrotum, and testicles. Females have a uterus, cervix, vagina, fallopian tubes, and ovaries.

FRAMEWORK AND WEATHERPROOFING

4
The **muscular system** is made up of three types of muscle—skeletal, smooth, and heart. It circulates blood around the body and enables it to move.

5
The **skeletal system** consists of bone, cartilage, and ligaments. It supports the body, protects the major organs, and also provides an anchor for the muscles.

6
The **integumentary system**—the skin—protects the body and helps to keep it at the correct temperature. The system is also the largest sense receptor, responding to touch, pressure, heat, and cold.

WIRING AND CONTROL

7
The **nervous system** contains the brain and the nerves. The brain receives electrical signals from the body via nerves and quickly sends back a response.

8
The **endocrine system** controls body processes. It releases floods of chemical messages called hormones into the blood from glands around the body.

6

THE REPRODUCTIVE SYSTEM IS THE ONLY SYSTEM THAT THE BODY CAN SURVIVE WITHOUT.

INSTRUCTIONS

PIPING

9 The **respiratory system**—the airways and lungs—takes air into the lungs to supply oxygen to the body. It also breathes out the waste gas, carbon dioxide.

10 The **circulatory system** includes the heart and the network of blood vessels. It carries blood from the heart to all the body cells, and back again. Blood circulates continuously around the body.

11 The **lymphatic system** is the body's "sewage" works, draining excess fluid and debris from the immune system. It contains a network of tubes that run throughout the body.

12 The **immune system** defends the body against invading germs and repairs damage. It includes barriers, such as the skin, white blood cells, and antibodies.

WILD Landscape

Powerful microscopes have revealed the surface of the body to be surprisingly varied. Close-up, skin looks like rough terrain and hair grows on it like a forest. The skin is such an important organ that it receives more than one third of the body's blood supply.

ROLLED OUT FLAT, YOUR SKIN WOULD COVER 21 SQ FT (2 SQ M). IT WEIGHS 9 LB (4 KG).

Hair-raising

Humans are one of the few land mammals to have almost bare skin, so we wear clothes to keep warm. This bare skin, however, helps to keep the body cool. The 100,000 hairs on our heads grow faster than anything else on the body—and under a microscope they look like bumpy tree trunks.

▲ Although just 2 mm thick, the skin is made of various layers.

Scalp hairs grow 2–3 mm each week. Each hair grows for three to five years before it falls out, and a new hair starts to grow.

Mighty overcoat

The skin is the biggest organ in the body and has many important functions. It's waterproof and germproof, insulates the body from the cold and lets out excess heat, responds to touch, and gives the body nourishment by soaking up vitamin D from sunlight.

Shedding skin

To stay effective, skin has to be continually renewed. New cells push up from the dermis to provide the outer layer of protective dead cells in the epidermis. The body loses 40,000 of these dead cells every minute. In a human's lifetime, nearly 100 lb (50 kg) of skin is lost.

Nailing it

Just like hair, nails are made from a tough material called keratin, created when certain cells die and harden. Fingernails grow about 1.5 in (3.5 cm) a year—so, uncut, they could grow 10 ft (3 m) or more in a lifetime. The middle fingernail grows fastest and the thumbnail grows slowest.

▼ The nail plate—the visible part of the nail—is made of a hard, transparent type of keratin.

The outer layer of the skin, or **epidermis**, is a tough coating of overlapping layers of dead skin cells.

Underneath, in the **dermis**, there's a thicker layer containing glands, nerve endings, and touch sensors.

Under that, there's a blanket of fat, called "**subcutaneous fat**," to keep the body warm.

The dermis and fat layers are well supplied with **blood**.

▲ As old skin cells die, they leave a hard protein called keratin on the outside of the skin. Keratin gives the skin a tough, protective outer coat, which eventually flakes off.

GROWING SKIN

Artificial skin can be grown in laboratories. It is used to treat people who have suffered severe burns or skin diseases, as well as for testing the effects of drugs and cosmetics.

▼ Each piece of artificial skin is usually grown from a tiny piece of human skin.

CELLULAR Cosmos

The body is made up of 100 trillion microscopic parcels called cells. They come in many shapes and sizes as soft cases of chemicals, each with its own personal set of life instructions in the form of DNA.

SCIENTISTS ESTIMATE THAT ONLY FIVE PERCENT OF THE BODY'S CELLS BELONG TO THE BODY—THE REST ARE BACTERIA.

SOME TYPES OF CELL AUTOMATICALLY DIE WHEN THEY BECOME DAMAGED.

THE CELL ZOO

There are more than 200 different kinds of body cell, such as fat cells and skin cells, each with its own special task. The smallest cells are granules in the brain, and the longest are nerve cells that run through the spinal cord from the brain to the toes.

BLOOD CELLS
carry oxygen around the body.

MUSCLE CELLS
contract to enable the body to move.

NERVE CELLS
carry messages between the brain and the body.

BONE CELLS
make bone harden as it forms.

SPERM CELLS
carry the male's genes to the egg.

OVUM CELLS
contain the female genes, ready for fertilization.

THE SMALLEST CELLS ARE RED BLOOD CELLS AT ONLY 0.0075 MM ACROSS.

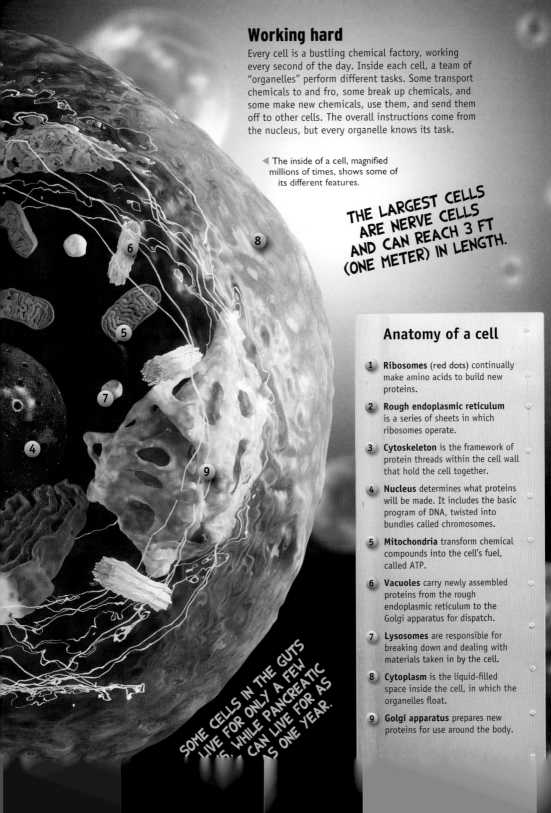

Working hard

Every cell is a bustling chemical factory, working every second of the day. Inside each cell, a team of "organelles" perform different tasks. Some transport chemicals to and fro, some break up chemicals, and some make new chemicals, use them, and send them off to other cells. The overall instructions come from the nucleus, but every organelle knows its task.

◀ The inside of a cell, magnified millions of times, shows some of its different features.

THE LARGEST CELLS ARE NERVE CELLS AND CAN REACH 3 FT (ONE METER) IN LENGTH.

SOME CELLS IN THE GUTS LIVE FOR ONLY A FEW ...S, WHILE PANCREATIC CAN LIVE FOR AS ...S ONE YEAR.

Anatomy of a cell

1. **Ribosomes** (red dots) continually make amino acids to build new proteins.

2. **Rough endoplasmic reticulum** is a series of sheets in which ribosomes operate.

3. **Cytoskeleton** is the framework of protein threads within the cell wall that hold the cell together.

4. **Nucleus** determines what proteins will be made. It includes the basic program of DNA, twisted into bundles called chromosomes.

5. **Mitochondria** transform chemical compounds into the cell's fuel, called ATP.

6. **Vacuoles** carry newly assembled proteins from the rough endoplasmic reticulum to the Golgi apparatus for dispatch.

7. **Lysosomes** are responsible for breaking down and dealing with materials taken in by the cell.

8. **Cytoplasm** is the liquid-filled space inside the cell, in which the organelles float.

9. **Golgi apparatus** prepares new proteins for use around the body.

CHEMICAL Plant

The body is made from a mixture of water and organic chemicals, and contains more than half the known chemical elements in the Universe. Every part of the body is involved in changing one chemical to another.

You're wet

The body is more than 60 percent water, found both in cells and body fluids such as blood and lymph. Without water for chemicals to dissolve in, vital reactions could not take place.

You're fat

Much of the body is simply fat. "Essential fat" is needed for particular body tasks—making up 3–5 percent of men's bodies and 8–12 percent of women's. "Storage fat" is fat built up as adipose tissue to give the body an energy reserve. Pads of fat also help to keep out the cold and act as shock absorbers.

▲ Adipose cells are packed with lipids (fat), which store emergency energy reserves.

You're strong

Chemicals called proteins make up about 20 percent of the body. Some proteins are building materials—every cell and tissue is part-protein, including muscles, bones, tendons, hair, nails, and skin. Other proteins make chemical reactions happen (enzymes), send chemical messages (hormones), fight infection (antibodies), or carry oxygen in the blood (hemoglobin).

▶ Blue and red fluorescent dyes show up the protein in throat tissue.

You're sweet

Carbohydrates provide fuel, either circulating in the blood ready for action as simple sugars, or stored as glycogen in the liver and the muscles.

◀ The uterine gland in a pregnant woman's womb secretes glycogen to give the egg energy to grow.

You're made to plan

Nucleic acids are the body's programmers. Deoxyribonucleic acid (DNA) in every cell, passed on from your parents, stores the instructions that tell the body not only how to grow, but also what to do throughout life.

▶ A sample of DNA that has been extracted from body cells.

You're a mineral mine

Bones are partly made of the minerals calcium and phosphorus. Calcium and sodium in the blood, and phosphorus, potassium, and magnesium in the cells, are essential for chemical processes. Iron is crucial to hemoglobin, which carries oxygen in the blood. Traces of other minerals are also vital, including cobalt, copper, iodine, manganese, and zinc.

▶ The calcium in cheese (magnified here) strengthens bones.

You're a gas

The body contains gases, such as oxygen, carbon dioxide, nitrogen oxide, hydrogen, carbon monoxide, and methanethiol. Some are dissolved in fluids and others are bubbles of gas in the lungs or gut.

BODY CHEMICALS

About 99 percent of the mass of the human body is made up of just six elements:

CHEMICAL	%	FOUND
Oxygen	65%	Liquids and tissues, bones, proteins
Carbon	18%	Everywhere
Hydrogen	10%	Liquids and tissues, bones, proteins
Nitrogen	3%	Liquids and tissues, bones, proteins
Calcium	1.5%	Bones, lungs, kidney, liver, thyroid, brain, muscles, heart
Phosphorus	1%	Bones, urine

VITAL Juice

Blood is the body's multitasking transport system. It not only delivers oxygen from the lungs to every body cell, it also carries food to fuel and maintain the cells, and washes away waste to the liver, kidneys, and lungs for disposal. Blood rushes immune cells into action to guard against infection, and even helps to spread body heat.

▼ Scabs are the body's way of protecting a wound from infection.

Plugging a leak

When you cut yourself and bleed from the damaged blood vessels, platelets instantly gather. As they do, they send out an alarm in the form of "clotting factors." These draw in other platelets and encourage them to clump together to make fibers or "fibrin" that plug the leak. The fibrin dries out to form a scab, protecting the wound until it has healed.

Fresh Frozen Plasma (CPD-A1)

129169J 6

COMPLEX MIXTURE

Blood looks red in color, but it is mostly made up of a clear, yellowish fluid called plasma. The color red comes from the red blood cells that are swept along by it. Plasma also contains giant white cells called leucocytes and little lumps called platelets.

O RhPOSITIVE

▲ Blood cells and fibrin (yellow) rush to a wound to form a clot. This is called coagulation.

▼ Blood vessels have muscular walls that control the flow of blood around the body.

Super pipes

Blood circulates through millions of blood vessels—tiny pipes that thread through the body. From the heart, they branch out from wide arteries into narrow arterioles, and then even narrower capillaries. On the way back to the heart, blood vessels gather in narrow venules and then wider veins.

A mighty pump

The heart is a tireless pump, made almost entirely of muscle. Its muscular walls contract and relax about 70 times a minute, pushing all the blood around the body once every 90 seconds. The heart has two sides—the right side is smaller and weaker, and pumps blood only to the lungs. The stronger left side pumps blood around the whole body.

Seeing red

Button-shaped red blood cells contain a special chemical called hemoglobin, which carries oxygen around the body. The average person has 25 trillion red cells, and the body makes two million new ones every second.

◄ An arteriogram is an X-ray where a special dye is used to detect the heart's blood vessels.

The body cannot survive for long without the continuous input of energy from food. Energy drives all the body's chemical reactions, which release heat energy for warmth and muscle energy for movement.

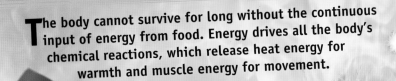

▼ Some cells only contain one mitochondrion, but others contain thousands.

◀ A thermogram detects heat. Red shows the hottest parts and blue the coldest. The head and chest are the warmest parts of the body.

A trillion fires

Tiny bursts of energy are constantly released inside each of the trillions of body cells in a process called cellular respiration. In each cell, microscopic "furnaces" called mitochondria use oxygen to break down glucose molecules and release energy. This process generates heat.

STORED ENERGY IS PACKED INTO MILLIONS OF TINY MOLECULES CALLED ATP (ADENOSINE TRIPHOSPHATE). ATP IS LIKE A COILED SPRING, READY TO UNWIND AND RELEASE ITS ENERGY.

Hot bodies

For body processes to function well, the body must remain at the perfect temperature—98.6°F (37°C). This is warmer than the outside world, so the body continually generates heat by moving the muscles and triggering chemical reactions in the liver.

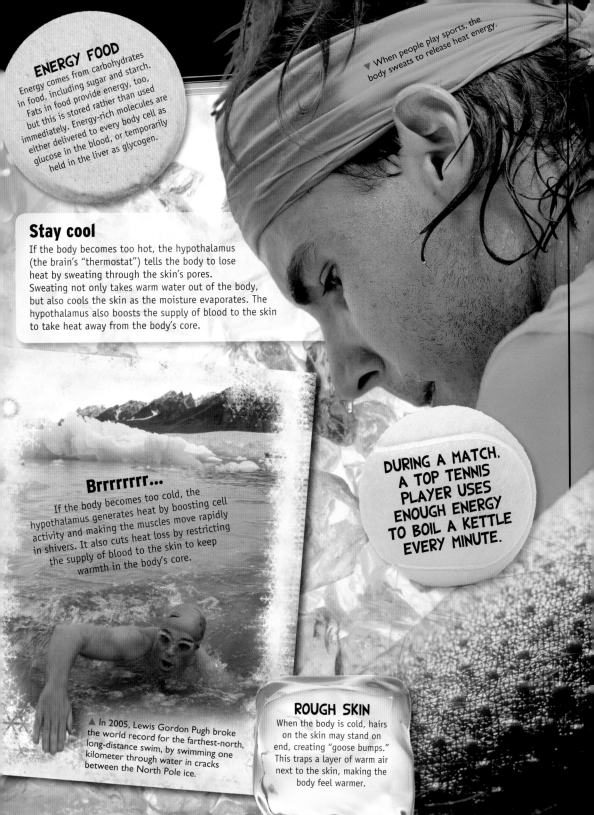

ENERGY FOOD

Energy comes from carbohydrates in food, including sugar and starch. Fats in food provide energy, too, but this is stored rather than used immediately. Energy-rich molecules are either delivered to every body cell as glucose in the blood, or temporarily held in the liver as glycogen.

▼ When people play sports, the body sweats to release heat energy.

Stay cool

If the body becomes too hot, the hypothalamus (the brain's "thermostat") tells the body to lose heat by sweating through the skin's pores. Sweating not only takes warm water out of the body, but also cools the skin as the moisture evaporates. The hypothalamus also boosts the supply of blood to the skin to take heat away from the body's core.

Brrrrrrrr...

If the body becomes too cold, the hypothalamus generates heat by boosting cell activity and making the muscles move rapidly in shivers. It also cuts heat loss by restricting the supply of blood to the skin to keep warmth in the body's core.

▲ In 2005, Lewis Gordon Pugh broke the world record for the farthest-north, long-distance swim, by swimming one kilometer through water in cracks between the North Pole ice.

DURING A MATCH, A TOP TENNIS PLAYER USES ENOUGH ENERGY TO BOIL A KETTLE EVERY MINUTE.

ROUGH SKIN

When the body is cold, hairs on the skin may stand on end, creating "goose bumps." This traps a layer of warm air next to the skin, making the body feel warmer.

Human COMPUTER

The brain contains more than 100 billion nerve cells, or neurons. Each neuron is connected to as many as 25,000 other neurons—creating trillions of routes for signals to buzz around the body. This enables us to think and learn, jump and sit, and laugh and cry—everything that makes us human.

RECEIVING SIGNALS

The cerebral cortex is the wrinkled layer of interconnected nerve cells around the outside of the brain. It is made up of different structures, each with individual functions. Many sense signals are received and responded to here.

The demanding brain

The brain makes up less than two percent of the body's weight, yet demands more than 20 percent of its blood supply. Deprived of the oxygen blood carries for even a few moments, brain cells quickly die. If the blood supply is cut off entirely, the brain loses consciousness in ten seconds and death occurs within a few minutes.

◀ Blood floods into the brain continuously through large arteries to give it energy for thinking.

PREFRONTAL CORTEX

is involved with memory, solving problems, and judgment.

A brain of two halves

The brain is split into two halves or hemispheres, linked by a bundle of nerves. The left half controls the right side of the body and the right half controls the left side of the body. It is believed that the left side deals with logical and analytical thinking, while the right side expresses emotion and creativity.

LEFT HEMISPHERE

RIGHT HEMISPHERE

Frontal lobe

Parietal lobe

Temporal lobe

Occipital lobe

▶ When reading, the most active areas are in the left hemisphere, at the brain's language centers.

The gray matter

The cerebral cortex is sometimes called the "gray matter." It's where most conscious thoughts occur and its folds allow a number of nerves to be packed into a small space. Scans have revealed that it contains "association areas"— areas that become more active while we're doing certain tasks.

LIMBIC SYSTEM processes smells, emotions, and memories, which is why smells can evoke memories.

MOTOR CORTEX controls the movement of muscles around the body.

SENSORY CORTEX registers sense signals from around the body such as pressure, heat, and pain.

WERNICKE'S AREA controls the understanding of both spoken and written words.

VISUAL CORTEX analyzes what the eyes see.

HIPPOCAMPUS is involved with moods, willpower, recognizing new experiences, and short-term memory.

ON AVERAGE, A FEMALE'S BRAIN WEIGHS 2.5 PERCENT OF HER BODY WEIGHT, AND A MALE'S 2 PERCENT.

HYPOTHALAMUS controls body temperature, water levels, and blood flow. It also triggers feelings such as hunger and anger.

CEREBELLUM is the plum-sized extension of the brain that controls the body's balance and posture, and coordinates movement.

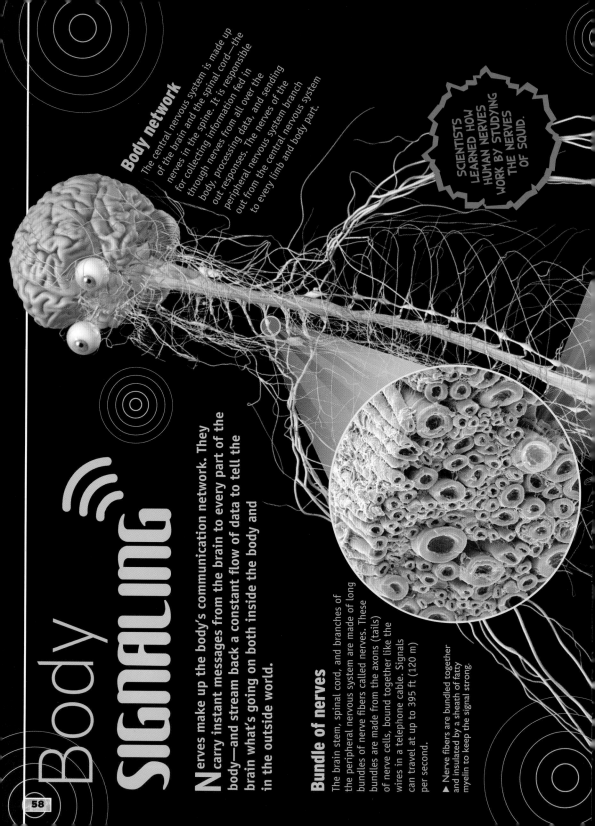

Body SIGNALING

Nerves make up the body's communication network. They carry instant messages from the brain to every part of the body—and stream back a constant flow of data to tell the brain what's going on both inside the body and in the outside world.

Bundle of nerves

The brain stem, spinal cord, and branches of the peripheral nervous system are made of long bundles of nerve fibers called nerves. These bundles are made from the axons (tails) of nerve cells, bound together like the wires in a telephone cable. Signals can travel at up to 395 ft (120 m) per second.

▶ Nerve fibers are bundled together and insulated by a sheath of fatty myelin to keep the signal strong.

Body network

The central nervous system is made up of the brain and the spinal cord—the nerves in the spine. It is responsible for collecting information fed in through nerves from all over the body, processing data, and sending out responses. The nerves of the peripheral nervous system branch out from the central nervous system to every limb and body part.

SCIENTISTS LEARNED HOW HUMAN NERVES WORK BY STUDYING THE NERVES OF SQUID.

Living connector

A nerve cell, or neuron, is shaped like a spider, with a nucleus at the center, lots of branching threads called dendrites, and a winding tail called an axon. From each neuron, electrical signals buzz through the dendrites, along the axon, and out to other neurons.

▲ Nerve signals are transmitted as waves of electrically charged potassium and sodium particles.

AUTOPILOT

Reflexes are muscle movements that happen without conscious thought. Humans are born with some of these automatic movements, such as urinating. Others are learned, such as drinking from a glass without thinking about it.

TOUCH ME

You might think you have just five senses—sight, hearing, smell, taste, and touch. However, the skin is covered with at least five kinds of sense receptor. There are different receptors for pain, heat, cold, touch, and pressure. Some receptors, called Pacinian receptors, respond quickly and then stop, while others, called Ruffini receptors, respond slowly but then keep going.

Mind the gap

Neurons don't touch each other. Instead, they transmit signals across a tiny gap or "synapse." Droplets whenever a nerve signal arrives. Droplets of neurotransmitter lock onto the receiving neurotransmitter into the synapse. As the droplets of neurotransmitter, they fire the signal onward. As the droplets of neurotransmitter, they fire the signal onward. As the nerve's receptors,

▼ There are thought to be 100–500 trillion synapses in the brain.

EYE OPENER

YOUR AWESOME EYES COMBINE THE PICTURE QUALITY OF THE BEST DIGITAL CAMERAS WITH A VERSATILITY THAT NO CAMERA CAN MATCH. THEY CAN FOCUS BOTH ON A SPECK OF DUST INCHES AWAY AND A GALAXY FAR ACROSS THE UNIVERSE, AND WORK IN BOTH STARLIGHT AND SUNLIGHT.

1 -
2 -
3 -
4 -
5 -
6 -
7 -
8 -
9 -
10 -

Ǝ Ш Ш Ǝ Ш Ш
20/70

Ш Ǝ Ш Ǝ Ш Ǝ Ш Ǝ
20/50

Black hole

The dark "pupil" is a porthole that lets light into the eye. It looks black because the eye is so dark inside. When light gets very dim, the fringe or "iris" around it can open wide to let more light in.

▼ The pattern of fibers in the iris is unique to each human, so it can be used to identify individuals, just like fingerprints.

▼ A damaged cornea can cause blurred vision. To restore normal eyesight, surgeons lift the top layer of the cornea and trim it minutely with a laser.

Stay sharp

The cornea is the transparent window at the front of the eye that gives the main focusing power. Light rays pass through the cornea and are refracted (bent) before hitting the lens. The lens adjusts the focus to give a sharp picture, whether you are looking at something close-up or far away. Each adjustment takes barely one fiftieth of a second.

Movie time

The inside of the eyeball is like a mini cinema. The cornea and lens project an image onto the back of the eye, called the retina. Although the image is just a few millimeters across inside the eye, you see it at its real size.

THE EYES CONSTANTLY SCAN THE SCENE YOU ARE LOOKING AT IN INCREDIBLY RAPID MOVEMENTS TO BUILD UP A PICTURE AND PICK OUT KEY DETAILS.

▲ When the muscles surrounding the lens contract, the lens becomes thicker and can focus on close-up objects.

▶ There are only seven colors in the rainbow, but the eye's cones can distinguish ten million colors!

Taking the picture

The retina acts like the photocells in a camera—150 million rods detect if it's dark or light, and even work in very low light, while eight million cones detect colors and work best in daylight.

Highway to the brain

It's actually the brain that "sees," not the eyes, using the visual cortex. When light hits the retina, the rods and cones send nerve signals down the optic nerve to create a picture in the brain.

▶ Signals from the right side of each retina go to the right of the visual cortex; those from the left of each retina go to the left of the visual cortex.

61

NEW Life

The human body can create a new version of itself. It starts when two single, microscopically tiny cells—a male's sperm cell and a female's egg cell—join. From this combined cell a new life begins, as a baby slowly grows inside the female's womb for the nine months of pregnancy.

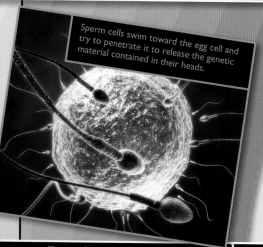

Sperm cells swim toward the egg cell and try to penetrate it to release the genetic material contained in their heads.

AFTER ONLY ONE WEEK, THE EMBRYO CONTAINS HUNDREDS OF CELLS.

Fertilized egg to embryo

As soon as the sperm and egg join successfully, the egg is fertilized, and the new life is "conceived." The egg immediately begins to divide rapidly, making seemingly identical copies of itself to create an embryo. As the cells multiply, differences appear, and layers that will become skin and organs develop.

Day 1

Millions try, but in most cases, only one sperm cell will succeed and fertilize the egg cell.

Day 6

The ball of cells attaches to the lining of the female's womb.

Day 40

In the beginning

The sperm and egg are special not because they have something extra, but because they have something missing. Unlike other body cells, they have only one set of 23 chromosomes, not the usual two. The sperm must add its 23 chromosomes to the egg's 23 chromosomes to make the full complement of 46 and start a new life. This happens during sexual intercourse, when the male's sperm swim into the female's womb to reach the egg.

IF TWO EGGS ARE RELEASED AT THE SAME TIME AND ARE BOTH FERTILIZED, NON-IDENTICAL TWINS DEVELOP.

The fertilized egg divides to form a small bundle of cells.

Embryo to fetus

After about 40 days, the embryo, though barely as big as a pea, has developed some recognizable features, such as a nose, mouth, and ears. Dark spots show where the eyes will grow. A heart beats rapidly inside, and a brain, muscles, and bones start to grow. After nine weeks, the embryo has become so babylike (though with a giant head) that it is described as a fetus, not an embryo.

At this early stage, the embryo looks like a tadpole.

The fetus turns upside-down with its head toward the entrance of the womb, ready to be born.

Growing strong

At the halfway stage, the fetus looks like a curled-up baby, only smaller and less defined. It's only about the size of an adult's hand, so still has some way to grow, but it begins to move around and may even kick its developing legs inside the mother's womb. Research suggests the baby may even be able to hear things outside its mother's body.

Time for birth

Finally, after about 37 weeks, the fetus is fully developed. Birth begins when the mother goes into "labor." Firstly, the womb muscles contract and burst the bag of fluid that surrounds the baby. Secondly, the muscles around the womb's neck contract and relax rhythmically to push the baby out through the birth canal.

The embryo is now about 5 mm long and buds for the arms and legs start to develop.

Day 133

The fetus is now about 6.5 in (16 cm) long and fine, downy hair covers its body.

Day 266

The fetus is about 14 in (36 cm) long and has a firm grip.

An ultrasound scanner reveals the baby growing inside the womb.

THE YOUNGEST BABY TO BE BORN AND SURVIVE WAS ONLY 21 WEEKS OLD.

GROWTH Factor

The rate at which the body grows depends on age and gender—babies and teenagers grow rapidly, and males become taller than females. Body proportions also develop with age—a baby's legs only make up one quarter of its length, but by adulthood the legs equal half of the body's height.

Big head

A newborn baby's head is already three-quarters of its adult size because it contains the brain. There are two gaps called fontanelles between the bones of a baby's skull, where there is only membrane (a "skin" of thin tissue), not bone. This allows the skull to flex, so there is room for the brain to grow even more. The gaps close and the bones join together after about 18 months.

BABIES HAVE A MUCH STRONGER SENSE OF SMELL THAN ADULTS.

Time to grow

Children grow quickly because the brain is continually sending out a "grow-faster" chemical. This growth hormone is secreted by the pituitary gland in the center of the brain. It tells cells to make protein and break down fat for energy. Too much growth hormone can cause a condition called gigantism, or acromegaly where the body grows too big and in the wrong places.

6 months–1 year

A baby begins to grow teeth—the upper and lower incisors come first.

1–4 years

Toddlers start to talk from one year old and can read simple words from four years old.

9–13 years

◀ For the first nine months or more, babies can only move on their hands and knees.

◀ Toddlers only gradually develop the strength and balance to walk upright.

Big changes

Puberty is the time of life when humans mature sexually. This process begins at about ten years old for girls and 13 for boys. During puberty, girls grow breasts and pubic hair. The hips grow wider and a new egg is released every month, in a cycle called menstruation. Boys grow pubic and facial hair, and the testes grow and start to produce sperm. By the time a boy is 15 or so, the testes make 300 million sperm a day.

◀▼ As boys grow, they develop more muscle than girls.

▶ Humans become shorter as they get older because the vertebrae in their backs become more compressed.

FRENCHWOMAN JEANNE CALMENT (1875–1997) LIVED FOR 122 YEARS AND 164 DAYS.

◀ Adult men are on average 6 in (15 cm) taller than women.

During adolescence a boy grows about 3.75 in (9.5 cm) a year and a girl 3.35 in (8.5 cm).

20+ years

Early adulthood is from 20 to 39 years and "middle age" is from 40 to 59 years.

60+ years

In old age, eyesight and hearing often weaken.

All grownup

By the age of 20, the body is fully developed and at its physical peak. By the early 30s, the body begins to lose strength, speed, and agility. Between the ages of 45–55, most women go through the menopause and become unable to get pregnant naturally.

Old age

As the body grows older, it stops renewing itself so well—the muscles weaken, bones become more brittle, joints stiffen, and the skin starts to slacken and wrinkle. The hair may eventually turn gray as pigment cells stop working.

MUSCLE
Power

Every move the body makes needs muscles, from lifting a finger to jumping in the air—even for sitting still. Without muscles, the body would slump like a sack of potatoes. Muscles are amazing little motors that work instantly, whenever they are needed, by constantly contracting and relaxing.

IF ALL THE MUSCLES IN THE BODY PULLED TOGETHER, THEY COULD LIFT A BUS.

Running on air

Ideally, muscles work aerobically—the cells get enough oxygen from glucose to release energy. However, if a person is unfit or has worked the muscles too hard, the cells may burn glucose "anaerobically"—without oxygen. This uses up glucose rapidly, making the body tired and leaving a buildup of lactic acid, which makes the muscles sore. To draw in the extra oxygen needed to burn this lactic acid, you pant when you stop running.

Outside and in

The body has two kinds of muscle—voluntary muscles that are under conscious control and involuntary muscles that work automatically. Voluntary muscles cover the skeleton and allow the body to move. Involuntary muscles control bodily functions, such as the heartbeat.

▲ The walls of the heart are made of cardiac muscle.

Power stripes

Muscles get their power from bundles of fibers that contract and relax. Inside each fiber are alternating, interlocking stripes or "filaments" of actin and myosin. When the brain tells a muscle to contract, little buds on each myosin filament twist, pulling on the actin filaments and making the muscle shorter. Each time a muscle contracts, another muscle fiber needs to shorten in the opposite direction to pull it back to its original length.

▶ Muscles work in pairs of actin and myosin filaments because they can only shorten themselves.

THE STRONGEST MUSCLES ARE THE MASSETER MUSCLES, WHICH CONTROL THE JAW'S BITING MOVEMENT.

▲ The body has several layers of muscle. Most are attached to bones with tough fibers called tendons.

Muscle building

During exercise, the muscles grow larger. At first, the fibers simply grow fatter. With regular exercise, the body grows new muscle fibers, which means they become stronger. The blood supply improves, too, so the muscles can work longer without tiring.

▶ Fibers in the voluntary muscles move the bones.

On demand

There are 640 voluntary muscles on the skeleton. The brain can only consciously control combinations that work together, rather than individual muscles. The longest is the sartorius muscle at the front of the thigh, while the biggest is the gluteus maximus in the buttocks.

STRONG
Structure

Bones give the body a strong, rigid, light framework. Bone can stand being squeezed twice as much as granite and stretched four times as much as concrete. Yet it's so light that bone accounts for barely 14 percent of the body's weight.

A lasting framework

The skeleton is made of 206 bones. As living tissue, the bones are constantly replenished with new cells that grow in the bone's center, called the marrow. The skeleton is the only body part that survives long after death.

THE HAND AND WRIST HAVE ABOUT 30 SMALL JOINTS.

Living bones

Bones are packed with living cells called osteocytes. Each osteocyte sits in a little pocket called a lacuna, and is constantly washed in blood. Some, called osteoblasts, make new bone. Others, called osteoclasts, break down the old, worn-out bone. The soft spongy center or "marrow" of bone produces new blood cells.

The tiniest bone is in **the ear**. It's called the stirrup bone and is only 3 mm long.

▲ Inside osteoblast cells, lumps of calcium salts crystallize to make hard bone.

▼ This broken knee joint is pinned in place while the bones repair themselves.

Broken bones

Bones are strong, but they can break or "fracture." Most fractures heal—the body stems any bleeding, then gradually fills the gap with osteoblasts, which weave new bone across the break. The break may need to be straightened and the bone held in place with pins or a plaster cast to ensure it repairs in the right way.

The **appendicular skeleton** is the 126 bones that hang off the axial skeleton—the shoulders, arms and hands, and hips, legs, and feet.

The **axial skeleton** is the 80 bones of the upper body, including the skull, spine, ribs, and breastbone.

Bone strength

Bones are an engineering triumph. Being hollow makes them light. Their strength comes from a combination of flexible collagen fibers and honeycomb struts called trabeculae. Trabeculae are thin but perfectly angled to resist stresses.

◄ The network of trabeculae inside a bone make it both strong and light.

▼ The human foot has 26 bones and 33 joints for balance and mobility.

WITH EVERY STEP, THE THIGH BONE BEARS A CRUNCHING PRESSURE OF 450 LB PER SQ IN (31 KG PER SQ CM).

Mobile skeleton

The skeleton is strong and rigid, yet can bend. It's made of lots of separate bones that are linked by flexible joints. At the joints, bones are held together by fibers called ligaments and cushioned by smooth, rubbery cartilage.

ALIEN INVADERS

You might think you're clean, but you're actually a zoo of microscopic bugs. Living inside your guts are up to 1,000 different species of bacteria—and a similar number are encamped on your skin. Then there are fungi and viruses, mosquitoes, fleas, bedbugs, blackflies, botflies, lice, leeches, ticks, mites, and worms...

Very lice

The head louse (*plural* lice) is a tiny insect that has made human hair its only home for thousands of years. Lice are just big enough to see with the naked eye. They cannot fly, and spend all their lives crawling through their host's hair sucking tiny amounts of blood from the scalp.

Mite have

Your feet, wrists, genitals, and the roots of your hairs are home to a little bug—the follicle mite. Mites are related to spiders, but they are so small, even as adults (less than 0.25 mm long), that you can't see them with the naked eye.

◀ These tiny mites live in the roots of human eyelashes.

◀ The head louse spends its entire life in human hair.

IN 1991, DOCTORS REMOVED A 37-FT- (11-M-) LONG TAPEWORM FROM AMERICAN SALLY MAE WALLACE'S GUT.

Got you taped

In some parts of the world, people who have eaten uncooked meat end up with flat, ribbonlike tapeworms living in their gut. These worms settle in and feed off the food the infected person eats, soon making their host ill. They are so flat and the human guts are so long that they can grow to more than 30 ft (9 m) in length!

▲ The head of a tapeworm has suckers for gripping the inside of the gut.

Coli wobbles

About 0.1 percent of the bacteria living in the gut belongs to the strain *Escherichia coli*. Most *E coli* are harmless, but occasionally they can make you ill with food poisoning. They enter the body on unwashed vegetables or in uncooked meat, then multiply and release floods of toxins in the intestines.

▼ Under UV light, bacteria can be seen on the hands.

▲ E coli bacteria live in your gut and supply you with vitamins K2 and B1.

Skin bugs

A powerful microscope reveals your skin is absolutely crawling with tiny bacteria. Many are Actinobacteria, which are also common in soil. Although there are many billions of bacteria living on your skin, they are so small, their combined volume is no bigger than a pea.

MILLIONS ARE COMING!

BODY DEFENDERS!

THE BODY OFTEN COMES UNDER ATTACK FROM DISEASE-CAUSING BACTERIA, VIRUSES, AND OTHER GERMS. TO DEFEND AGAINST THESE ONSLAUGHTS, THE BODY IS ARMED WITH AN AMAZING SERIES OF BIOLOGICAL WEAPONS, KNOWN AS... **THE IMMUNE SYSTEM.**

I'M GOING TO MAKE YOU SUFFER!

Bacteria cause diseases such as whooping cough, tetanus, and typhoid.

THE VILLAINS

Germs cause illness when they invade or "infect" the body and multiply.

Viruses are tiny and cause diseases such as colds, flu, mumps, rabies, and AIDS.

Sometimes, germs beat the outer defenses and get inside the body to start their nasty work.

OUTER DEFENSE

Like a fortress, the body has lots of barriers and booby traps to stop germs getting in. The first barrier is the skin.

KEEP OUT!

WE'RE IN! TIME TO CAUSE SOME DAMAGE...

When germs sneak in, they get bogged down in slimy mucus in the nose and lungs—and blasted out with a sneeze or cough. The stomach vomits germs out!

Germs make you feel ill with the toxins they release. Plus, the body's battle against these intruders can cause fever, aching joints, and inflammation. It's time for the inner defenses to get ready...

FIRST INNER DEFENSE

Floods of little "complement" proteins mob the intruding germs.

WHAT?!?

They send out an alarm to the body, which causes soreness and inflammation.

SEND IN THE SPECIALS!

PHAGOCYTES

Troops of "special forces" are called in—the phagocytes. There are three types of phagocyte—granulocytes, dendritic cells, and macrophages.

MACROPHAGE

GRANULOCYTE

DENDRITIC CELL

Repair
and
Rebuild

The body is remarkably good at shielding itself against harm and repairing any damage. Sometimes, though, it needs medical help. Vaccines arm the body's immune system against future infections, antibiotic drugs kill many disease-causing bacteria, and surgery corrects defects.

▶ This titanium knee joint (red) replaced a knee destroyed by bone disease.

New joints

Bones are tough, but can be damaged, especially at the joints. With the aid of special materials such as titanium, surgeons can remove a damaged joint and replace it with an artificial one that lasts for ten years. By using a computer to visualize the replacement, it is always a perfect match.

▼ Scottish firefighter Ian Reid, who lost his hand in an accident, has a bionic replacement that can grip as tightly as a real hand.

Bionic bodies

Artificial hands and limbs respond to nerve signals directly from the brain. Therefore a person only has to think to control the tiny electric motors that make a bionic, or prosthetic, hand move. Bionics are used to replace lost or irreversibly damaged hands or limbs. In the future, soldiers may have extra bionics to give them "super powers."

ADD-ON POWERED LIMBS COULD ENABLE A SOLDIER TO RUN UP A HILL CARRYING MORE THAN 650 LB (300 KG).

▶ This replacement bladder was grown on a mold from stem cells in just five weeks.

Organ growing

Scientists can now make replacement body parts in the laboratory. They start with special "stem" cells that can grow into any kind of cell. The stem cells form into the right shape on a special mold of microfibers. Once the new organ has grown, the mold dissolves and the organ can be transplanted into the body.

Disease control

Many deadly diseases have been brought under control using vaccination. This is where the body is infected with a weakened or "dead" version of a germ. In response, the body builds up antibodies, so it is ready to fight back if ever exposed to the real disease.

New cells for old

Stem cells can grow into almost any other kind of cell. In the future, stem cells may be produced to make cells that replace faulty ones. Scientists may then be able to treat anything from cancer to multiple sclerosis, blindness, and even baldness.

◀ Faulty organs might be repaired by using stem cells from embryos such as this three-day-old human embryo.

▲ Smallpox caused about 400 million deaths during the 20th century. It was finally eradicated by vaccination in the 1970s.

IN 2011, A MAN WAS GIVEN A NEW THROAT GROWN FROM STEM CELLS—THE FIRST LAB-GROWN REPLACEMENT ORGAN.

CHEMICAL Messengers

How does the body know when to grow and by how much? How does it cope with stress? How does it keep thousands of substances in the right balance? The complex task of controlling the body is managed by an extraordinary system of chemicals called hormones.

Stop & Go

Hormones work automatically using clever "feedback" systems. The liver supplies the blood with the energy chemical glucose. If glucose levels rise too high, the pancreas releases the hormone insulin, which feeds back to the liver, triggering it to stop supplying glucose.

▲ Islets of Langerhans cells in the pancreas release hormones to control sugar levels in the blood.

▶ Thyroglobulin (shown in orange) makes thyroid hormones to control the body's energy usage.

Hormones and glands

Hormones are chemicals that have particular effects on certain cells. "Endocrine" glands release tiny drops of hormone into the blood to spread around the body. Each gland releases its own type of hormone, and each hormone has a special task.

THE PITUITARY GLAND WEIGHS LESS THAN ONE GRAM, BUT IT IS ONE OF THE MOST IMPORTANT ORGANS IN THE BODY.

Grow-faster chemicals

The thyroid gland in the neck and pituitary gland in the brain are no bigger than cherries, but supply vital hormones to make sure the body grows normally. The three thyroid hormones control how fast cells burn energy. The pituitary gland makes the growth hormone, which controls how fast cells grow and multiply.

▶ Too much growth hormone can make the body grow unusually big. Sultan Kösen has the largest handspan in the world at 12 in (30.5 cm) wide.

▶ During extreme bungee activities, the body releases hormones jumping to prepare for "fight or flight."

Adrenaline rush

A sudden scare prepares the body for danger, as it triggers a flood of the hormones adrenaline and noradrenaline. As the hormones rush into the blood, they make the heartbeat faster and stronger. This boosts the blood supply to the muscles to help you run or fight. The blood supply to the skin is restricted, making it go pale and cold. The eyes widen, giving better vision.

ARTIFICIALLY MADE STEROID HORMONES CAN BE USED IN INHALERS TO REDUCE THE EFFECTS OF ASTHMA.

▶ When blood is evaporated, the sex hormone testosterone is left behind as crystals.

Time for change

At a certain age, known as puberty, sex hormones start to be released into the body. A female's ovaries make estrogen and progesterone, which control the menstrual cycle. A male's testes make testosterone, which promotes the production of sperm and creates characteristics such as a deep voice and bigger muscles.

Wild
SCIENCE

Find out about extreme reactions and deadly materials. From highly corrosive acid to explosions inside stars, this is where science goes off with a bang.

◀ A high-speed photograph shows the explosive power of a bullet leaving the muzzle of a gun.

CRAZY Matter

Under normal conditions, such as those that exist on Earth, matter exists in three phases—solid, liquid, and gas. These phases can transform from one to another by changing the temperature and pressure. Matter can also exist in other more exotic phases, but only under the most extreme conditions.

◄ Inside a plasma globe, a high-voltage electrode turns gases into glowing plasma.

See-through solid

Unlike most solids, glass is amorphous—it does not have a crystal structure. With no crystal surfaces to interfere with the passage of light, glass is transparent. Some people believe that solid glass flows very slowly, like a liquid, but this is just a myth. Glass is a true solid because it has a definite shape and volume.

3.6 million °F
(2 million °C)

2,700°F
(1,500°C)

Pulsing plasma

Plasma, the fourth state of matter, is made of electrically charged atoms and electrons. In nature, plasma is found in extremely high-energy situations such as lightning bolts and stars. Man-made plasmas are used in street lighting and neon signs. Plasma technology can produce bright light from very little electricity.

▲ When glass is melted, it forms a thick, rubbery liquid that can be shaped.

Low-energy gas

Bose-Einstein condensate is a fifth phase of matter named after the two mathematicians who proposed its existence. Scientists prepare a condensate by cooling a dilute gas to within a thousandth of a degree from absolute zero (-459.67°F, -273.15°C). At this very low temperature, the atoms in the gas are at their lowest possible energy state and behave in strange ways.

LIGHT TRAVELING THROUGH A BOSE-EINSTEIN CONDENSATE IS SLOWED TO ABOUT 37 MPH (60 KM/H) AND MAY EVEN STOP ALTOGETHER.

◀ Lasers are used to cool the atoms of gas to make a Bose-Einstein condensate.

Glass container

Laser beam

-459.67°F (-273.15°C)

-296°F (-182°C)

Dry ice

When carbon dioxide gas freezes at -109.3°F (-78.5°C), it is known as "dry ice" because it does not melt into a liquid. Instead, it sublimes—turns from a solid to a gas without going through the liquid phase. Liquid carbon dioxide can only exist under conditions of more than five times normal atmospheric pressure.

-109.3°F (-78.5°C)

▶ Scientists believe that methane clathrate could be used as an energy source in the future.

▲ Dry ice is often used to refrigerate frozen goods for transportation. It freezes quickly and doesn't leave messy liquid behind.

Ice that burns

Methane is a highly flammable gas that solidifies at -296°F (-182°C). However, it can become part of solid water ice at the higher temperatures found in Arctic permafrost or beneath the seabed. Tiny bubbles of methane become trapped between crystals of frozen water to form a substance known as methane clathrate, or fire ice. If you set fire to it, the methane burns while the ice melts.

In the air

We live at the bottom of the atmosphere, surrounded by a mixture of gases called air. As air, these gases are essential to support life. Individually, however, gases such as oxygen and hydrogen reveal a savage and unforgiving nature.

The big H

The first element in the periodic table, hydrogen is the simplest and lightest. Air contains only a tiny amount of hydrogen—0.000055 percent! Hydrogen is lighter than air, so it was used to fill passenger airships in the early 20th century. Unfortunately, hydrogen has another property —it is highly flammable. After several fatal disasters, hydrogen airships were abandoned.

1	H
	Hydrogen
	1.01

▶ Filled with flammable hydrogen, the Hindenburg airship burst into flames in 1937, killing 36 passengers and crew.

Life-giving oxygen

Oxygen gas makes up 21 percent of air and without it, life would not exist. Living organisms depend on oxygen because it helps the body to convert food into energy. As one of the most reactive elements, it is often found as part of a chemical compound. Its reaction can be gradual—when a layer of oxide slowly forms on the surface of metal. Or it can be extremely rapid and energetic—when an entire building burns ferociously.

Safe or not?

Nitrogen is the most abundant gas in air, making up 78 percent. An inert gas, it does not react easily with other elements. However, in a process called fixation, nitrogen combines with other substances to make compounds including nitrates. These compounds are used by plants to convert energy into food, to help them grow. Scientists discovered how to produce synthetic nitrogen compounds in the 1880s. These are now produced on an industrial scale to make both fertilizer and explosives.

▲ A nitrogen-based explosive, such as TNT, was used to demolish this high-rise building.

Glowing gas

Neon makes up only 0.0018 percent of air. Neon is a noble gas—it does not react with other elements. However, it does react to electricity. When an electrical current is passed through a gas discharge tube containing neon, the noble gas turns into brightly glowing plasma. It is used to make cities fluoresce with colored light.

▲ Neon signs light up New York City, U.S. Neon tubes can be any shape or size and neon gas itself gives off an orange-red light.

◄ To extinguish fire, firefighters douse the flames with water to remove the heat, so the fire can no longer burn.

10	
Ne	
Neon	
20.18	

8	
O	
Oxygen	
16.00	

7	
N	
Nitrogen	
14.01	

Toxic pollutant

A less abundant form of oxygen called ozone has three oxygen atoms instead of the more usual two, making it even more reactive than that oxygen. High in the atmosphere, the Sun's harmful rays—ozone forms a layer that protects Earth's surface from harmful ultraviolet rays. However, when pollutant ozone occurs near Earth's surface, it is a harmful pollutant that attacks the respiratory system.

► Ozone is one of the toxic ingredients in photochemical smog—toxic air pollution formed by air pollution.

ACTIVE Metals

Most of the elements in the periodic table are metals, and many are safe to handle. An aluminum or iron pan, for example, can be heated on the stove or washed in water without a reaction occuring. Other metals, such as sodium and magnesium, react to air, water, and heat with violent chemical fury.

CESIUM IS A PALE-GOLDEN METAL THAT EXPLODES IF IT COMES INTO CONTACT WITH ICE.

▲ When sodium reacts with water, it produces a bright yellow-orange flame.

11
Na
Sodium
23.00

GONE IN A FLASH

Francium is an unstable metal that decays so rapidly, it almost doesn't exist. Scientists estimate that there is only about one ounce (28 g) of francium in Earth's crust. Any amount of this metal big enough to be visible immediately vaporizes in the heat produced by its decay. The largest mass of francium that scientists have ever assembled weighed a mere 300 million billionths of an ounce (0.0000000000000000016 g).

Sodium sizzle

A silver-colored metal, sodium is soft enough to be cut with a table knife. But drop a piece of sodium into water and it reacts furiously, fizzing and dashing around the surface. The exothermic reaction produces heat as well as hydrogen gas. The heat quickly ignites the hydrogen, causing an explosion.

▼ This lump of rock contains a few scattered atoms of francium.

87
Fr
Francium
223.00

Potassium perils

Only small amounts of potassium and water are needed to produce a reaction that gives off enough heat to ignite the hydrogen released. Powdered potassium ignites spontaneously when exposed to air, so it must be stored in mineral oil. If potassium is exposed to air for a long period, its surface becomes coated with a layer of pressure-sensitive superoxide that may explode at the slightest touch.

12
Mg
Magnesium
24.31

▲ Magnesium burns with an intense white light.

Burning bright

Although magnesium is a highly reactive element, on contact with air, it forms a less-reactive oxide layer. This enables it to be stored and handled with safety. Magnesium ignites very easily. It burns so brightly that it was once used by photographers to provide the "flash" for their cameras.

19
K
Potassium
39.10

▼ A distinctive purple flame indicates the presence of potassium vapor.

Dangerous decay

Radium reacts fiercely with water, but that is nothing compared to its other dangers. Discovered by Nobel Prize winner Marie Curie (1867–1934), radium is a heavy, unstable element that slowly decays. This decay produces large amounts of radioactive energy. Long-term exposure leads to diseases such as cancer, tumors, and leukemia.

88
Ra
Radium
226.03

▲ Radium generates so much energy that it glows in the dark. It was once used to paint clock faces, making them luminous.

▶ Marie Curie carried out radium experiments without any protection. She later died of aplastic anemia caused by exposure to radioactivity.

Hazardous HALOGENS

Dangerous, highly reactive elements are lurking in every room of your home and on every shelf in your local store. No need to panic! The products are completely safe—when used correctly. But if you don't respect the halogens, proceed at your peril...

CHLORINE

Poisonous to all forms of life, green-colored chlorine gas is the only element to have ever been used as a weapon—when it was released onto battlefields during World War I (1914–1918). When breathed in, it reacted with water in the lungs to produce hydrochloric acid, which dissolved lung tissue. However, chlorine's killer nature also works as a lifesaver. Used in disinfectants and at water purification plants, it kills dangerous microorganisms before they can do serious harm.

Deadly iodine

Iodine is a dark, shiny solid. Minute amounts are essential for a healthy diet and occur naturally in many foods, such as strawberries. When dissolved in alcohol, iodine is used as an antiseptic and disinfectant; it was also used in the manufacture of photographic film. However, large amounts are poisonous and iodine vapor is toxic, causing breathing problems.

▲ Iodine turns from a solid into a poisonous violet-colored gas at room temperature.

53	
I	
Iodine	
126.90	

9	
F	
Fluorine	
18.998	

Fierce fluorine

Poisonous and dangerously reactive, fluorine gas must be handled with care. It is so unstable that on contact with water, it spontaneously burns with a bright flame. However, fluorine is part of useful products, too. It is one of the main components of refrigerants used in household fridges and freezers. Surprisingly, fluoroplastics—plastics containing fluorine—are some of the most stable man-made substances, widely used for electrical insulation.

199.99

17 Cl Chlorine 35.45

▼ Some halogen bulbs contain bromine. They produce brighter light, use less energy, and last longer than normal lightbulbs.

Bad bromine

Although it is now considered too dangerous to be used in pesticides, bromine is still added to disinfectants for hot tubs and spa pools. Bromine has an unusual property —it interferes with combustion reactions— making it perfect for fire-retardant materials.

▼ Sodium metal burns and glows when added to chlorine gas.

35 Br Bromine 79.90

▼ At room temperature, bromine is a dark-brown poisonous liquid that rapidly evaporates into an orange gas.

Tiny amounts of chemicals containing fluorine, known as fluorides, are added to drinking water and toothpaste to make our teeth stronger and more resistant to decay.

LETHAL Liquids

A cids are savage solutions that produce hydrogen ions when dissolved in water, conduct an electrical current, and taste slightly sour. Strong acids are corrosive chemicals, powerful enough to dissolve metal and stone. Weak acids are irritants, causing blisters on contact with skin.

DISSOLVING GLASS

Hydrofluoric acid is highly corrosive and must be stored in plastic containers because it dissolves most materials, including glass and metal. This trait is put to good use, however, as hydrofluoric acid is used to etch words and images onto glass. Extreme caution and care must be taken when using hydrofluoric acid; as well as causing severe burns to exposed skin, it is also deadly poisonous.

Emergency crews require special training and equipment to deal with exposure to acids and other hazardous materials.

RISKY SPILLS

A highly dangerous, colorless liquid, hydrochloric acid is produced by bubbling hydrogen chloride gas through water. A strong acid, it is widely used in the manufacture of plastics and household cleaning agents. Its fumes are irritating to the lungs and contact with the skin causes chemical burns. With more than 20 million tons produced and transported annually, accidental spillages sometimes occur.

DISSOLVING GOLD

Gold became known as the royal metal not only because of its rarity and beauty, but also because it could not be dissolved or tarnished by acid. That is until aqua regia, a mixture of hydrochloric acid and nitric acid, was developed. Aqua regia is used in gold mining to dissolve the metal out of gold-bearing rock. The mixture of acids and dissolved gold is then chemically treated to obtain the pure gold.

79
Au
Gold
196.97

Gold in concentrated hydrochloric acid

Gold in concentrated nitric acid

Gold in aqua regia

◀ The brownish tinge in the right-hand tube shows that gold has dissolved in the "royal water."

▼ Karst landscapes, such as the Shillin Stone Forest in Yunnan, China, form naturally from years of carbonic acid exposure.

SHAPING THE LAND

Rainwater absorbs minute amounts of carbon dioxide as it falls through the atmosphere, turning it into weak carbonic acid. Although harmless to plants and animals, the acid passes through small cracks in rocks. Over time, this dissolves the limestone rock, shaping it into peaks and caverns.

Pollution!

When fossil fuels such as coal are burned, they release sulfur dioxide gas into the atmosphere. This gas reacts with water vapor to produce weak sulfuric acid, which falls to Earth as rain. Acid rain is strong enough to kill trees and poison wildlife in lakes and streams.

▶ Acid rain damages stone statues and buildings.

TOP 10

TOXIC ROCKS

Earth's crust contains many valuable and useful minerals, but some of them can also be extremely harmful to living things—and the dangers are far from obvious. Unlike poisonous animals, toxic minerals do not carry a warning about the dangers they represent.

1 THALLIUM

A soft, silvery metal, thallium is used in the electronics and glass industries. Chemicals containing thallium were once widely used as insecticides and rat poison, but they were banned for being too dangerous. It caused damage to the internal organs and nervous system, as well as death.

81 **Tl** Thallium 204.38

3 BERYLLIUM

This strong, lightweight metal has a high melting point and is ideal for many industrial applications, such as the manufacture of aircraft and computers. Unfortunately beryllium has major drawbacks—it is rare, expensive, and toxic. It can cause a pneumonialike illness, as well as skin diseases.

4 **Be** Beryllium 9.01

2 ARSENIC

Arsenic was once used to preserve wood and in agricultural products. But any substance containing arsenic is deadly to all living things, apart from a few unusual bacteria. Short-term contact causes sickness and diarrhea. Long-term exposure causes multiple organ failure and death.

33 **As** Arsenic 74.92

4 PHOSPHORUS

Phosphorus is essential to life because it adds strength to bones and teeth. But it is far from friendly. Chemicals containing phosphorus are among the deadliest poisons ever made. After a short period, joint pain is experienced. Longer exposure leads to weak bones and kidney damage.

5 CADMIUM

This highly toxic metal is rare in Earth's crust, but is widely used to make rechargeable batteries because it doesn't easily corrode. If inhaled, it can damage the lungs. If consumed, it irritates the stomach, causing vomiting and diarrhea. Long-term effects include kidney disease and fragile bones.

48 **Cd**
Cadmium
112.41

7 ASBESTOS

A naturally occuring mineral, asbestos was once widely used for building insulation because it is incombustible. However, asbestos was outlawed in many countries around the world in the 1980s when it was discovered that inhaling asbestos dust caused deadly lung diseases.

10 ANTIMONY

This silvery metal is usually found combined with sulfur as kohl—a black substance that is easily crushed to form a slightly greasy powder. The ancient Egyptians used kohl as an eye cosmetic, not realizing that even small doses of this toxic metal can cause headaches and nausea.

51 **Sb**
Antimony
121.75

6 CERUSSITE

This innocent-looking mineral is easily converted into "white lead," a substance that was once used in paints and cosmetics to give them opacity. Unfortunately, lead is extremely poisonous, especially to children, and is now considered too dangerous to be used in household products.

15 **P**
Phosphorus
30.97

9 CINNABAR

An important ore of mercury, cinnabar is often found near recent volcanic activity. This soft mineral can be ground up to make a rich red-colored pigment called vermillion. It can also be heated to produce the highly toxic element, mercury. Contact can cause shaking, nerve damage, and death.

8 SELENIUM

The human body needs minute quantities of selenium and it is found in some foods, such as nuts and fish. Larger doses are toxic. Minor symptoms of selenium poisoning include bad breath, fever, and hair loss. Serious effects include nerve damage, organ problems, and even death.

34 **Se**
Selenium
78.96

SUPER CARBON

ONE ELEMENT CAN TRANSFORM ITSELF INTO DIFFERENT FORMS, EACH WITH UNIQUE AND AMAZING PROPERTIES. IS IT IRON? IS IT CALCIUM? NO, IT'S CARBON! DEPENDING ON HOW THE CARBON ATOMS ARE ARRANGED, IT CAN EXIST AS DIAMOND, THE HARDEST KNOWN SUBSTANCE, OR AS GRAPHITE AND CHARCOAL, WHICH ARE SOFT AND POWDERY.

DIAMOND
20 TIMES HARDER THAN STEEL!

INDESTRUCTIBLE AND SPARKLING

DEEP BENEATH EARTH'S SURFACE, HEAT AND EXTREME PRESSURE TRANSFORM CARBON INTO **DIAMOND**! WITH CARBON ATOMS LOCKED IN AN IMMOVABLE LATTICE, DIAMOND'S TRANSPARENT CRYSTALS ARE HARDER THAN ANY OTHER KNOWN NATURAL SUBSTANCE. BLASTED TO EARTH'S SURFACE BY VOLCANIC EXPLOSIONS, ITS UNIQUE PROPERTIES MAKE DIAMOND THE ULTIMATE ALLOTROPE (FORM) OF CARBON. DIAMOND CAN CUT THROUGH ANYTHING, ONLY MELTS AT A SUPERHOT 6,420°F (3,550°C), REFLECTS ALL FORMS OF LIGHT, BLOCKS ELECTRICITY, AND SURVIVES EXTREME PHYSICAL, CHEMICAL, OR RADIOACTIVE FORCES. PLUS DIAMOND FORMS BEAUTIFUL, GLITTERING GEMSTONES THAT PEOPLE WILL PAY MILLIONS TO GET THEIR HANDS ON!

BUCKYBALL

IMMUNE TO SEVERE IMPACT!

STABLE AND VERSATILE

BURSTING ONTO THE SCENE IN 1985, ALL-ROUNDER BUCKYBALL—FULL NAME, **BUCKMINSTERFULLERENE**—IS THE RESULT OF A SCIENTIFIC EXPERIMENT GONE RIGHT! ITS HOLLOW CAGELIKE STRUCTURE OF 60 CARBON ATOMS ALLOWS IT TO CAPTURE AND CARRY OTHER ATOMS. DEPENDABLE BUCKYBALL WILL NOT REACT WITH ANY CHEMICAL OR DISSOLVE IN WATER. LIGHT AND STRONG, BUCKYBALL IS A HEAT CONDUCTOR, AN ELECTRICAL INSULATOR, AND STOPS LIGHT IN ITS TRACKS.

THE FUTURE IS STRONGER, HARDER, AND LIGHTER

ONLY ONE ATOM THICK, 300 TIMES STRONGER THAN STEEL, HARDER THEN DIAMOND, TRANSPARENT, SUPERFLEXIBLE, AND AN EXCELLENT CONDUCTOR OF HEAT AND ELECTRICITY... WHAT IS THIS MAN-MADE SUPERMATERIAL? **GRAPHENE**! DISCOVERED IN 2004, ITS CARBON ATOMS ARE ARRANGED IN A FLAT HONEYCOMB STRUCTURE, GIVING IT THE STRONGEST BONDS KNOWN TO SCIENCE.

GRAPHITE

WITHSTANDS EXTREME TEMPERATURES OF SPACE!

SLIPPERY AND SOFT

CRUSHED AND HEATED UNDERGROUND, CARBON-RICH ROCKS MUTATE INTO METAMORPHIC ROCK AND **GRAPHITE** IS BORN! ITS CARBON ATOMS FORM SHEETS THAT SLIDE OVER EACH OTHER WITH EASE. THIS SLIPPERY PROPERTY MAKES IT A PERFECT LUBRICANT FOR FREEING SURFACES TRAPPED TOGETHER BY FRICTION. AN INCREDIBLE HEAT SHIELD, GRAPHITE RESISTS SCORCHING TEMPERATURES OF 5,400°F (3,000°C). GRAPHITE IS USED AROUND THE WORLD EVERY DAY—AS THE SOFT "LEAD" IN PENCILS.

COOL Cryogenics

Matter—solids, liquids, and gases—can be heated to millions of degrees, but cannot be cooled below -459.67°F (-273.15°C). This temperature is absolute zero and as substances approach it, they stop acting as they normally do and exhibit strange properties.

▼ Aluminum foil covers *Ariane 5*'s fuel tanks to protect the fuel from external heat build up.

Powerful combination

Inside a typical liquid-propellant rocket, such as *Ariane 5*, liquid oxygen below -297°F (-183°C) and liquid hydrogen below -423°F (-253°C) are kept in separate tanks. At liftoff, they are fed into a reaction chamber where they ignite, producing enormous amounts of heat and thrust to power the rocket into space.

▲ Human cells, such as egg and sperm cells, are stored in liquid nitrogen to preserve them until they are needed.

Cold storage

Extreme cold has the same effect on living tissue as extreme heat —it kills, but with an important difference. Heat destroys living structures, whereas cold preserves them. Medical researchers preserve specimens in liquid nitrogen because slow freezing can damage the tissues. Liquid nitrogen reaches temperatures of -320.33°F (-195.74°C) so rapidly that water in the cells cannot form crystals. Some scientists believe that it is possible to preserve entire human bodies. Known as cryonics, more than 100 people have been stored this way, but no one has been revived.

Liquid helium is a vital part of Magnetic Resonance Imaging (MRI) scanners. It cools the superconductive magnets inside, allowing an electric current to flow through them without any resistance. This creates a magnetic field that helps doctors to build accurate and detailed images of inside the human body.

▼ A soccer player uses a cryogenic cylinder before a game to reduce any swelling caused by injury.

Freezing therapy

Some athletes use low-temperature cryogenic chambers to recover from injury. Wearing nothing but socks, gloves, earmuffs, and a bathing suit—to protect against frostbite—they spend up to three minutes in a small room or container cooled by liquid nitrogen, at temperatures of about -256°F (-160°C). The low temperature causes the body to release endorphins, which speed recovery. It also numbs the body's nerves, providing immediate pain relief and reducing any swelling.

▼ MRI scanners use magnetic fields and radio waves to produce images of soft body tissues, such as a fetus.

WHEN COOLED TO -455°F (-270°C), HELIUM BECOMES A SUPERFLUID THAT FLOWS UPHILL.

CRYOSURGERY

Liquid nitrogen is often used to remove unwanted tissue such as warts, tags, and moles from the skin. Only small amounts are needed because the freezing effect is so rapid, destroying the unwanted tissue in only a few seconds. Known as cryosurgery, this process is much quicker than the traditional surgeon's scalpel and leaves no scarring on the skin.

▲ Tiny amounts of liquid nitrogen are passed through a fine probe onto a wart to freeze and kill it.

Under PRESSURE

Pressure is measured in pascals and normal atmospheric pressure on Earth is about 101 kPa (14.7 psi). We understand the characteristics that substances possess and the way in which they behave at normal pressure. When put under greater pressure, the same substances often behave in sudden and unexpected ways.

Dollar bill on a surface

1 Pa

Gentle breeze

Popping corn

10 Pa

Water boiling at room temperature

2 kPa

2.6 kPa

Atmospheric pressure for Earth at sea level

101 kPa

Air pressure in a car tire

250 kPa

Impact of a punch

350 kPa

An average human bite

1.1 mPa

30 mPa

30 mPa
Deep-sea dive
The increased pressure, even during a fairly shallow dive, forces extra gas into a diver's blood. If the diver surfaces too quickly, bubbles of nitrogen may form in the blood. This causes dizziness and a painful and potentially fatal condition known as "the bends." At greater depths, the pressure has a crushing effect on the whole body.

These polystyrene cups were identical until one was taken to a depth of about 9,850 ft (3,000 m). The pressure at this depth—equivalent to 300 atmospheres—compressed the cup to a fraction of its original size.

◀ Water jet cutters are safer for firefighters because they can make holes for the main jet of water without getting too close to the flames.

70 mPa

Chamber pressure of a gun firing

Water jet cutter

690 mPa

Under enough pressure, water can cut through concrete, metal, and solid rock. A water jet cutter uses high-speed electric pumps to produce a narrow jet of water driven by pressures up to 690 mPa (100,000 psi)—almost 7,000 times atmospheric pressure. The jet can cut to depths of 18 in (45 cm) and can be as narrow as 0.076 mm—about the width of a human hair.

110 mPa

Bottom of the Mariana Trench, 7 mi (11 km) below sea level

690 mPa

Meteorite impact

2 gPa

When a 300,000-ton, iron meteorite smashed into Arizona 50,000 years ago, it did more than produce a spectacular crater. The pressure created by the sudden impact was so great, it transformed the minerals in the surrounding rocks.

2 gPa

◀ The crater measures 600 ft (183 m) in depth and 3,900 ft (1,200 m) in diameter.

▼ The liquid metal inside Jupiter can conduct heat and electricity.

Making metallic hydrogen

200 gPa

Scientists believe that the gravity of Jupiter creates so much pressure that hydrogen starts to behave like a metal. To make metallic hydrogen in a laboratory, scientists must achieve pressures of more than 2 million times atmospheric pressure.

1
H
Hydrogen
1.01

The Planck Pressure—only ever reached shortly after the Big Bang or in a black hole

200 gPa   **360 gPa**   **4.6x10^{113} Pa**

Crude Crackdown

Crude oil is like black gold—a chemical treasure containing hundreds of useful substances. After oil has been extracted from the ground, it is subjected to harsh treatment to obtain the maximum by-products from this precious commodity.

The ingredients

Crude oil comes from the ground. It is formed from the remains of animals and plants. Over millions of years, these remains are covered in layers of mud and rock, creating great heat and pressure. These conditions turn the remains into crude oil, a mixture of hydrocarbons.

FRACTIONING COLUMN

77°F (25°C)

FRACTIONS DECREASE IN DENSITY AND BOILING POINT

CRUDE OIL

FRACTIONS INCREASE IN DENSITY AND BOILING POINT

660°F (350°C)

BURNING OIL

HOME | NEWS | CONTACT

Crude oil is flammable and oil-well fires can occur through human accidents or natural events such as lightning strikes. Due to the enormous fuel supply, the jets of flames are difficult to extinguish. Firefighters detonate explosives to create a shockwave that pushes the burning fuel and oxygen away from the unburned fuel—like blowing out a huge candle!

The breakdown

The mixture is separated by heating the oil inside tall metal towers. This process is called fractional distillation, popularly known as "cracking." Near the top of the tower, the first substances to be released are liquid petroleum gases. Lower down, kerosene and heating oil evaporate and condense for collection. At the bottom of the tower, solids such as wax and asphalt are gathered.

Along with gases such as methane and pentane, BUTANE is mainly used as a fuel for cooking stoves.

BUTANE

Liquid NAPTHA is mainly converted to gasoline, but is also used as an industrial cleaning agent.

GASOLINE for cars and small trucks is by far the most precious product obtained from crude oil.

GASOLINE

Jets are the only engines that can burn KEROSENE efficiently. It is also used in heating stoves.

We rely on DIESEL engines in trains and large trucks to move goods over land.

Engines and other machines require a thin coating of LUBRICATING OIL to keep parts moving smoothly.

LUBRICATING OIL

Ships have special engines that burn FUEL OIL. It is also used for home-heating furnaces.

BITUMEN is used on roads and roofs.

BITUMEN

ABOUT 20 GAL (75 L) OF GASOLINE CAN BE PRODUCED FROM ONE BARREL—42 GAL (159 L)—OF OIL.

Top 10 global oil reserves

COUNTRY	BARRELS (IN BILLIONS)
Venezuela	297
Saudi Arabia	265
Iran	151
Iraq	143
Kuwait	102
United Arab Emirates	98
Russia	79
Libya	47
Kazakhstan	40
Nigeria	37

BURNING
Issue

Combustion occurs when a substance reacts with oxygen to produce large amounts of heat. Only gases actually burn. Solids and liquids must be heated until they vaporize before they will catch fire. Some substances spontaneously burst into flames, but most fires need an ignition source.

▼ Matches use the heat produced by friction to initiate a reaction between two chemicals—in the match head and on the side of the box. The flame produced ignites the wooden stem.

Invisible danger

Flashovers usually occur in confined spaces when a small fire produces enough heat to vaporize inflammable materials. This creates lighter-than-air gases that become concentrated in the upper part of a room. Even though there are flames below, the gases do not ignite because there isn't enough oxygen. That is, until a window breaks or someone opens a door. The fresh supply of oxygen that enters the room causes flames to flash upward and across the ceiling, instantly turning the whole room into a raging inferno.

▶ Firefighters battle a flashover by directing jets of water at the ceiling.

ON EARTH

▲ A steel-worker uses an acetylene torch to slice through metal.

Oxygen boost

An ordinary flame, such as a burning match, is known as a diffusion flame. The oxygen required for combustion diffuses from the air into the flame. The heat and intensity of the flame is limited by the supply of oxygen. A much fiercer, hotter flame is obtained by injecting pure oxygen. A gas-torch, which mixes oxygen with the inflammable gas acetylene, produces a flame with a temperature of about 6,300°F (3,500°C). The flame is so hot, it can easily cut through steel.

PAPER WILL SPONTANEOUSLY BURST INTO FLAME IF IT IS HEATED TO A TEMPERATURE OF ABOUT 454°F (234°C).

Spontaneous combustion

Elements such as potassium and phosphorus are pyrophoric in their pure form—they react so strongly with oxygen in the air that they burst into flame. Although rarely encountered in everyday life, pyrophoric substances can be found in haystacks and compost heaps, causing them to suddenly burst into flame with no external cause.

▼ When bacteria in a haystack decomposes, it produces heat, which becomes trapped. The temperature of the hay eventually rises above its ignition point, causing it to spontaneously combust.

Gravity vs. Zero gravity

On Earth, flames stretch upward and taper to a point. The yellow part of the flame is made up of tiny glowing particles of soot that rise through convection, and against the force of gravity. In a zero-gravity environment (in space), flames are spherical, produce less soot, and are less yellow in color.

IN SPACE

Making a BANG

Bulky and smoky, gunpowder is limited as an explosive. A gunpowder explosion is an example of very rapid combustion, with a speed of up to about 1,300 ft/s (400 m/s). High explosives, which were first developed in the 19th century, do not combust—they detonate, producing a shockwave that travels at speeds of up to 29,550 ft/s (9,000 m/s).

Gaining by graining

To make gunpowder, powdered charcoal, sulfur, and potassium nitrate are mixed with water to form a thick paste, which is then rolled into thin sheets. Before the paste dries, the sheets are cut into tiny fragments called grains. Graining the gunpowder has three advantages. Equal-sized grains are easier to measure accurately. Small grains have a larger surface area, so they burn much faster than a solid lump. Finally, small spaces between the grains in a pile ensure that there is enough air for each grain to burn efficiently.

Magic mixture

The secret of making gunpowder was discovered in China 1,000 years ago when a mixture of charcoal, sulfur, and potassium nitrate, have powerful and explosive qualities. The newly discovered gunpowder was soon put to use—packed into bamboo tubes to make simple rockets and bombs.

Rainclouds often formed over battlefields, so people in the 19th century tried to use gunpowder explosions to make it rain during droughts.

Rocket launcher

A firework rocket is lifted into the air by a propellant. When the fuse burns into the rocket tube, it ignites the propellant, which launches the rocket upward. When the propellant has burned through, it ignites an explosive charge that scatters colored stars into the sky.

▲ A trained bee sits inside a specially designed cassette.

▲ Chrysanthemum fireworks produce stars in a perfect sphere. The brightness increases as it spreads across the sky.

SNIFFER BEES
Honeybees can be trained to recognize a particular scent, such as gunpowder. Trained bees are placed inside small machines rigged with digital cameras. When the bees detect the odor, they extend their proboscis, or tongue, ready for a food reward. The machine then reports the presence of explosives to a human operator.

Smoke of battle

Gunpowder weapons, such as cannon and muskets, made it almost impossible to see the enemy after the first few minutes of battle. Gunpowder produces thick smoke when it burns—and with hundreds of cannon and thousands of muskets all firing at once, battlefields soon became shrouded in smoke that reduced visibility to a few yards. The 19th-century invention of so-called "smokeless" powder, a type of high explosive, went a long way to solving this problem.

▲ A musket produced clouds of dense smoke with each shot.

Explosive
MINDS

Throughout history, scientists have devised methods and formulas to make bigger and better bangs, often making use of ordinary substances such as cotton, sawdust, and air.

False claim

English scholar Roger Bacon (c. 1214–1294) is sometimes credited with the invention of gunpowder. Although he describes a gunpowder explosion in one of his books and he spread word of its existence, Bacon did not invent it. It is most likely that he learned about gunpowder from the Chinese in Central Asia.

CHRISTIAN SCHOENBEIN

SOFT BUT DEADLY

The first high explosive was made from cotton wool. German-Swiss chemist Christian Schoenbein (1799–1868) treated cotton fibers with nitric acid to produce an explosive that was much more powerful than gunpowder. Although known as guncotton, it was too powerful to be used as a propellant in cannon and firearms.

ROGER BACON

ASCANIO SOBRERO

THE DYNAMITE KID

Swedish chemist and industrialist Alfred Nobel (1833–1896) was a fellow student of Ascanio Sobrero. He became obsessed with making nitroglycerine safer after his brother Emil was killed by an accidental explosion. Nobel discovered that absorbent clay or sawdust enabled nitroglycerine to be formed into small sticks that could be handled and transported without the danger of detonation. This new, safe explosive was named dynamite.

ALFRED NOBEL

DYNAMITE

DYNAMITE

HERMANN SPRENGEL

Kaboom!

Hermann Sprengel (1834–1906) invented "safe" explosives by only mixing the components—highly reactive fuels and substances containing oxygen—immediately before use. In 1885, the U.S. Army Corps of Engineers used 140 tons of this mixture to blow apart rocks at Hell Gate, near New York Harbor—one of the most powerful preatomic explosions.

Trinity tester

The atomic bomb was developed by the top-secret Manhattan Project during World War II (1939–1945). Working under the direction of Robert Oppenheimer (1904–1967), a team of scientists completed the first successful atomic explosion in July 1945, code-named the Trinity test.

Cool explosive

German engineering professor Carl Linde (1842–1934) was a pioneer of industrial refrigeration. In 1895 Linde liquefied air at a temperature of -319°F (-195°C). He then obtained liquid oxygen (LOX) by boiling away the nitrogen. When mixed with charcoal, LOX made a powerful explosive, which was widely used for coal mining until the 1950s.

CARL LINDE

ROBERT OPPENHEIMER

SPEEDING
Bullets

When a gun is fired, a propellant inside the bullet burns. This generates gas, which shoots the bullet down the barrel at about 1,000 ft/s (300 m/s). At this speed, the bullet has a lot of momentum and kinetic energy. On impact, the bullet's energy is transferred to its target—with devastating results.

Shotgun blast

A shotgun shell contains up to 500 spherical metal pellets, known as shot. Inside the shell, the shot is held in a plastic cup, separated from the propellant by lightweight wadding. When the gun is fired, expanding gases push the shell along the barrel. At the end of the barrel, the wadding and cup fall away and the shot begins to spread out.

I Wadding and shot leave barrel.

2 Propellant gases billow and disperse.

3 Plastic shot cup falls away.

4 Shot separates from wadding.

SLOW AND STEADY

One early attempt to produce a high-velocity antitank gun involved first slowing down the bullet. The WWII sPzB 41 gun fired a bullet that was larger than the muzzle of the gun. As the bullet traveled along the tapered barrel, it slowed down as it was squeezed to the right size. The expanding gases behind it developed high pressure and the bullet left the barrel with a much higher velocity—up to 4,600 ft/s (1,400 m/s).

▼ The squeeze gun had a range of about 1,600 ft (500 m).

Tank targets

Tank guns fire metal arrows, called penetrators, to pierce the 12-in (30-cm) armor of enemy tanks. The penetrators are enclosed in a lightweight plastic sheath that falls away when the penetrator leaves the muzzle at speeds of about 6,000 ft/s (1,800 m/s).

▲ A soldier loading armor-piercing penetrator ammunition onto a tank.

6

▶ This bulletproof glass has a layer of plastic between two layers of glass. The plastic makes this glass 100 times stronger than glass alone.

Stopping a bullet

Bulletproofing isn't possible—we can only provide protection against certain types of bullet. Modern body armor uses superstrong plastics such as Kevlar. A Kevlar vest will stop low-velocity handgun bullets. To stop high-velocity rounds, additional protection such as hardened ceramic plates are necessary. Some body armors also use gels that cause the kinetic energy of a bullet to spread out.

SHOCKING Power

Electricity is an invisible force that provides power for much of the world. An electric current is produced as electrons flow through a wire or jump through the air. When we see a spark, it's actually the air being turned into plasma by the power of electricity.

SHOCKING TOUCH

The shock you sometimes feel when you touch metal actually takes place a fraction of a second beforehand. Electricity normally travels through conductors such as metals, but not through insulators such as glass and air. However, electricity can jump between two conductors across a gap of insulating air—the higher the voltage, the greater the distance it can jump.

Caged safety

English scientist Michael Faraday (1791–1867) proved that if you surround yourself with a conducting network, such as a metal cage, electrical discharges will travel along the bars, leaving you unharmed—as long as you don't touch the sides! Faraday cages are used to protect electrical equipment from lightning strikes.

▲ A purple spark of static electricity jumps across the gap between two metal spheres.

▶ Touching the metal sphere of a Van de Graaff generator discharges a small amount of electricity, causing hair to stand on end.

▲ Safely inside a Faraday cage, this lab worker survived a 2 million-volt spark.

Power line maintenance workers rely on strict safety procedures to keep them from harm.

Megavolts

Invented by American electrical engineer Nikola Tesla (1856–1943), a Tesla coil can discharge sparks of million-volt electricity more than 10 ft (3 m) long. The highest voltages, up to 1.5 million volts, are produced at the upper part of the apparatus, which is shaped like a doughnut to maximize its surface area. Once used in radio transmission and to provide high voltages for neon lighting, the Tesla coil has now been replaced by modern electronics.

An Australian inventor used a Tesla coil to create this sparkling display around himself.

SHOCKPROOF

Maintenance crews are able to safely work on power lines that carry more than 100,000 volts of electricity. The helicopter that carries workers to a power line must be bonded to the line using a special metal rod. This makes electricity flow around the helicopter. From this point, the helicopter cannot touch anything else otherwise the workers onboard would be instantly electrocuted. The workers are then free to fix the line problems without any immediate danger.

Hair-raising invention

Invented by American physicist Robert Van de Graaff (1901–1967), a Van de Graaff generator is a simple device for producing high-voltage electricity. Inside the hollow metal sphere, a moving belt causes an electrical charge to build up. When this sphere is touched by a conductor, the electricity is discharged. Large Van de Graaff generators are used to produce the extremely high voltages needed by atom-smashing linear accelerators.

109

RADIATION Hazard

When unstable elements decay into other elements, they produce dangerous amounts of radioactivity. There are three types of radiation—alpha, beta, and gamma. Alpha and beta radiation consist of fragments of atoms, called subatomic particles, traveling at high speed. Gamma radiation is the most energetic form of light.

Beta beams

Beta rays are composed of minute specks of matter—electrons, the smallest of all stable particles—traveling at about 90 percent of the speed of light. These electrons, known as beta particles, can damage human tissue. But with little penetrating power, they can be easily blocked by 0.2 in (5 mm) of aluminum.

▶ Beta radiation is used by machines to control the thickness of materials such as plastic. If the plastic becomes too thick, it absorbs more radiation, which is detected by the Geiger counter. This prompts the rollers to move closer together.

Geiger counter

Plastic sheeting

Rollers

Source of beta radiation

Slow and steady

Alpha rays are composed of alpha particles, which are about 8,000 times bigger and heavier than beta particles and travel much more slowly at about 10,000 mi/s (16,000 km/s). Alpha particles are damaging to living tissue, but are so large and slow, they cannot penetrate the skin. They can be stopped by only a sheet of paper.

BETA β

ALPHA α

▲ A detector is worn by people who work with radiation on a daily basis.

ALUM

▶ The blue light is called Cerenkov radiation. It occurs in water because the charged particles are moving faster than the speed of light in water.

Paper

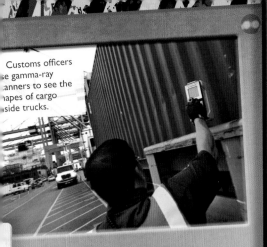
Customs officers use gamma-ray scanners to see the shapes of cargo inside trucks.

Piercing light

Gamma rays travel through matter almost as easily as ordinary light travels through glass—only blocked by lead that is several inches thick. When gamma rays pass through the human body, the high energy they carry causes tremendous damage. High doses cause radiation burns and rapid death; lower doses kill more slowly through cancer and other radiation-induced diseases.

GAMMA γ

LEAD

Nuclear electricity

A nuclear power station harnesses the energy produced by the decay of highly unstable elements, such as plutonium, and uses it to generate electricity. Although alpha, beta, and gamma rays are invisible, the level of radioactivity inside a nuclear power station is enough to make ordinary water glow with a blue light.

DISASTERS

CHERNOBYL, UKRAINE, APRIL 1986

In the evening of April 25, engineers began an experiment to see whether the cooling system could function if the electricity supply were to fail. This caused the reactor to overheat, fuel to explode, and fires to break out. The reactor was not protected by a concrete shell, so radioactive debris escaped into the atmosphere, carried for hundreds of miles by the wind.

▼ Found two years after the disaster, the quince fruit on the right has mutated to a much larger size.

FUKUSHIMA, JAPAN, MARCH 2011

When a tsunami struck the coast of Japan on March 11, it damaged the cooling system at the Fukushima nuclear power station. Without this, the nuclear fuel overheated and caught fire, releasing large amounts of radiation and radioactive material into the atmosphere. The radiation levels were so high that the authorities evacuated the entire area within 12 mi (19 km) of Fukushima.

▼ A woman from inside the evacuation zone is checked for radiation exposure.

Star
BIRTH

Stars are made from atoms of the two lightest elements, hydrogen and helium, drawn together by gravity. The actual moments of star birth are hidden by thick clouds of dust, but nothing can conceal the spectacular surroundings of these explosive events.

1   The Eagle nebula

Compressed gas

When a Giant Molecular Cloud reaches a large enough size, at least 1,000 times the mass of the Sun, it undergoes gravitational collapse—the cloud implodes and breaks up. Vast amounts of energy are released, creating shockwaves that compress and heat the fragments of the cloud to such an extent that nuclear fusion begins. The central region of each fragment becomes the core of a new star.

3   Orion nebula

Not-so empty space

The vast reaches of space between the stars are not completely empty. Each cubic inch (16 cu cm) of space contains about 16 atoms—usually hydrogen, sometimes helium, and occasionally another element. These atoms are not evenly spread because they tend to clump together in clouds. The biggest of these clouds are known as Giant Molecular Clouds (GMCs), and this is where many new stars are born.

2   Pleiades star cluster

Nebulous evidence

After a Giant Molecular Cloud has collapsed and produced stars, the remains can be seen as a bright nebula in the night sky. The young stars blast radiation into space—creating delicate glowing shapes that will eventually disappear after a few million years.

Scientists estimate that 95 percent of all the stars there will ever be have already been born.

Planetary formation

Announcing arrival

Young stars announce their presence by blasting twin, high-speed jets of material out in space. Dust and gas that fall toward the surface of a new star are swirled around and then ejected in long streams above the star's poles. The shockwave from these jets travels at more than 187 mi/s (300 km/s). As it smashes into surrounding gases, it causes them to glow brightly.

Bok globule

Starry globules

Bok globules—small, dense clouds of dust and gas that block light—were discovered last century by the astronomer Bart Bok (1906–1983). Astronomers believe that new stars can be formed inside Bok globules when dust and gas contract under the gravity of the clouds.

Stellar jets

New planets

When a new star blazes into existence, its gravity may pull dust and gas into a swirling protoplanetary disk around the star. After many collisions over time, the dust and gas clump together to form small planetesimals, which eventually combine to form planets. Astronomers have so far discovered more than 1,000 planets that orbit around stars other than the Sun.

Extreme
UNIVERSE

From a storm more than twice the size of Earth, to colliding galaxies and the fiery birth of a star—this tour of the Universe is guaranteed to make you feel tiny.

◀ The Orion Nebula is one of the nearest to Earth. It measures about 30 light-years across and contains 2,000 times more matter than is found in the Sun.

The Big Bang

Theory

The Universe is unimaginably big. It contains all the matter and energy we know about, and scientists are learning more all the time. The Big Bang Theory describes how the Universe began and expanded rapidly into the Universe that exists today.

▲ These four galaxies, called Stephan's Quartet, have been colored to show their red shifts. The three red galaxies are further away and traveling faster than the closer, bluer galaxy.

The Universe began with an enormous outpouring of energy from a microscopic point, called a singularity.

HOW DO WE KNOW THE UNIVERSE IS EXPANDING?

As distant galaxies move away from Earth, the light waves they give off are stretched out behind them, making them look red in color. This effect, called red shift, was first discovered by Austrian mathematician Christian Doppler in 1842. Edwin Hubble then showed that a galaxy's red shift is proportional to its distance from Earth. The further away a galaxy is, the greater its red shift and the faster it must be moving away from Earth. Massive red shifts reveal that the most distant objects in the Universe are flying away from Earth at astonishing speeds—often approaching the speed of light.

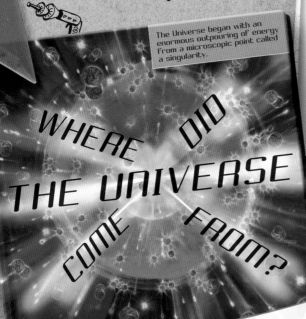

WHERE DID THE UNIVERSE COME FROM?

Scientists think the Universe was once smaller than a single atom. This tiny point is called a singularity. Then about 13.8 billion years ago, it burst out in all directions as a superhot fireball. This huge outburst is called the Big Bang. As the new Universe expanded, it cooled and some of its energy began to condense into the first particles of matter.

Can we see after-effects of the Big Bang?

Spacecraft have mapped the afterglow of the Big Bang, an echo of energy called the Cosmic Microwave Background that can still be detected today. Ripples in this energy led to the stars and galaxies that we see today. The Cosmic Background Explorer (COBE) spacecraft made the first map of it in the early 1990s. The most detailed map yet was made in 2010 by the Planck spacecraft.

MEGA COMICS

IS OUR UNIVERSE ALL ALONE?

YOU ARE HERE

OUR VAST UNIVERSE MIGHT BE JUST ONE OF MANY UNIVERSES IN A MULTIVERSE!

THE MULTIVERSE

A few years ago the Big Bang was thought to be the beginning of everything—time, space, energy, and matter. Scientists are now coming up with theories that, if correct, suggest that the Big Bang wasn't the beginning of everything, but just the beginning of our Universe—one of many. The theory of many universes is called the multiverse, but it has yet to be proven.

▼ The Planck spacecraft produced this map of radiation left over from the Universe when it was just 380,000 years old.

SCIENTISTS THINK THE MATTER WE CAN SEE FORMS ONLY 4 PERCENT OF THE UNIVERSE. THE REST IS DARK MATTER AND DARK ENERGY.

▲ This cluster of galaxies, called Abell 2744, is 3.5 million light-years away from us, so we see it as it looked 3.5 million years ago.

How far back can scientists look?

Scientists use modern telescopes to look back in time at distant galaxies—if a galaxy is one million light-years away from Earth, it will take one million years for the light waves to reach Earth. Therefore what we see is light that is one million years old! Astronomers have discovered galaxies that are 13 billion years old and gas clouds that are 12 billion years old, made up of the simplest elements—hydrogen and helium. They can work out the age of distant objects by analyzing light from them to find their red shift.

GALAXY
Gallery

Stars travel through space in giant groups called galaxies. There are billions of galaxies, each containing billions of stars. Galaxies are so vast and far apart that their sizes and the distances between them have to be measured in light-years—the distance light travels in a year.

Spiral

Elliptical

Irregular

Shape up

Galaxies are divided into three main groups according to their shape. About three-quarters of all galaxies are spiral shaped. They have a center called a hub and long, curved arms. If the center is rectangular, the galaxy is called a barred spiral. The next most common, called elliptical galaxies, are round or oval in shape and contain few new stars. Irregular galaxies have no definite shape and form when two galaxies collide.

Andromeda Galaxy

Hubble Ultra Deep Field

Our neighbor

One of the largest galaxies in the Universe is a spiral galaxy called Andromeda. Although it's about 2.5 million light-years away from Earth, it's so big that it can be seen with the naked eye. Andromeda is surrounded by more than a dozen dwarf galaxies that line up in a strange way—scientists can't yet explain why.

Teeming with galaxies

In 2004, the Hubble Space Telescope took a photograph of one tiny spot in space. The image was found to contain 10,000 of the most distant galaxies ever seen. Based on this, scientists worked out that the Universe could contain as many as 500 billion galaxies. Light from these galaxies travels across the Universe for about 13 billion years to reach Earth.

Cloud of creation

Nebulae are vast clouds of gas and dust within galaxies. They glow brightly, either because they are hot or because they are lit up by nearby stars. Dark nebulae are clouds of dust that block light coming from stars behind them. Inside nebulae are all the elements needed to form new stars, so some act as nurseries where new stars are born. The Eagle Nebula is 75 light-years across and has several star-forming regions within it.

Eagle Nebula

THERE ARE MORE THAN 7,000 KNOWN NEBULAE IN THE UNIVERSE.

Collision course

Occasionally, two galaxies collide. As the galaxies move through each other, the energy from the crash sends streams of gas and stars flying out into space. Sometimes, the two galaxies merge to form a new galaxy. The Milky Way is on a collision course with the Andromeda Galaxy, but the impact won't occur for 4 billion years. The Antennae Galaxies violently smashed into each other a few billion years ago, causing stars to be ripped from each galaxy to form an arc between them.

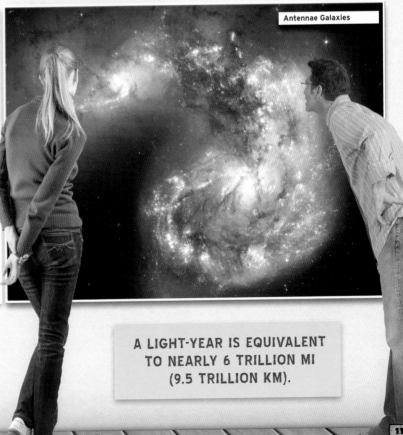

Antennae Galaxies

A LIGHT-YEAR IS EQUIVALENT TO NEARLY 6 TRILLION MI (9.5 TRILLION KM).

THE MILKY WAY

When you look into the night sky, the stars you see belong to our galaxy, the Milky Way. A barred spiral galaxy, it measures 100,000 light-years across and 1,000–7,000 light-years thick. Inside its clouds of gas and dust are more than 100 billion stars.

WHAT SHAPE?

From Earth, the Milky Way looks like a bright hazy band across the sky. This shows that the Milky Way is a flat, disk-shaped galaxy. All other galaxies of this shape are spirals, so scientists worked out that the Milky Way is a spiral galaxy.

▲ Earth is situated in one of the vast arms of stars curling out from the middle of the Milky Way.

FRIED EGGS

From the side, the Milky Way looks like a thin disk with a central bulge, sometimes described as looking like two fried eggs back-to-back. The bulge contains old stars and the disk contains younger stars. Dust clouds form a dark line that runs through the middle of the disk. The Sun is in the bulge, about two-thirds of the way out from the galaxy's center.

▲ A galaxy's spinning motion flattens it into a disk shape with a large ball of stars in the middle.

The Milky Way (left) and Andromeda (right) travel through space with a cluster of galaxies called the Local Group. Held together by gravity, this group contains more than 50 galaxies. Some of the largest clusters, such as the Coma, contain more than 1,000 galaxies. The Local Group and 100 other clusters make up the Virgo supercluster. There are millions of other superclusters throughout the Universe.

◀ The Local Group of galaxies is about 10 million light-years across.

◀ The disk of the Milky Way galaxy stretches across the whole sky, seen here from Dorset, U.K.

▼ The blue-white star, Kappa Cassiopeiae, is surrounded by a red bow shock of glowing gas.

Speed shock

As stars speed through space, particles flying off them smash into the dust and gas that float between the stars. If a star is traveling fast enough, the gas and dust collide so violently that they light up. A bright streak, called a bow shock, appears around the star and shows up most clearly at infrared wavelengths.

121

▶ One of the closest star clusters is the Pleiades or Seven Sisters.

◀ The Hipparcos satellite in space spent four years measuring the positions of 118,000 stars.

How far?

The distances between stars are immense. Apart from the Sun, the closest star to Earth—Proxima Centauri—is 4 light-years away. Astronomers have spent centuries measuring the positions of thousands of stars with greater precision. The Hipparcos satellite is the first spacecraft designed for precision astrometry.

Star clusters

Scientists know that stars are born in groups, or clusters, because they can see new stars forming close together. Large clusters contain as many as one million stars. Some clusters stay together for billions of years, while others drift apart after a few million years. Some stars are so close together that they orbit each other. Two orbiting stars are called a binary star.

Glow show

At the center of a star, the temperature and pressure are so great that hydrogen nuclei fuse together, forming helium nuclei. This reaction releases energy, which travels from the core to the star's surface—before causing it to glow—before radiating into space.

A STAR is Born

Each star twinkling in the night sky is actually a massive ball of searing-hot gas with a nuclear reactor in its core spewing out energy. The largest stars in the Universe are monsters, more than 1,500 times the size of our star, the Sun.

Convection zone

Radiative zone

Core

Photosphere

▶ A star like the Sun has a superhot core with a temperature of 27 million°F (15 million°C).

Hot colors

Blue stars are the hottest type of star. Their surface temperature is more than 40,000°F (22,000°C). Blue-white stars are almost as hot. One called Rigel has a temperature of 21,000°F (12,000°C). Orange-red stars are the coolest, and may be as cool as 3,100°F (1,700°C). Betelgeuse is a red star with a surface temperature of 5,500°F (3,000°C).

▲ The color of light given out by stars tells astronomers how hot they are.

Type of star	Surface temperature
O	Over 44,540°F (24,730°C)
B	19,340–44,540°F (10,730–24,730°C)
A	13,040–19,340°F (7,225–10,730°C)
F	10,340–13,040°F (5,725–7,225°C)
G	8,540–10,340°F (4,725–5,725°C)
K	5,840–8,540°F (3,225–4,725°C)
M	Less than 5,840°F (3,225°C)

Northern Hemisphere

Cancer
Gemini
Leo
Orion
Auriga
Ursa Major
Pole Star
Ursa Minor
Corona Borealis
Hercules
Taurus
Perseus
Andromeda
Cassiopeia
Cepheus
Lyra
Pegasus
Cygnus

PRETTY PATTERNS

People have divided the night sky into familiar patterns for thousands of years. They named the patterns, or constellations, after mythical figures and creatures. Different cultures chose different names. Ursa Major, the Great Bear, was seen as the leg of a bull by the ancient Egyptians and a mythical parrot by the Mayans. Today, the sky is divided into 88 internationally recognized constellations.

▶ The constellations range in size from the tiny Lyra to the giant Ursa Major.

Making stars

1. A supernova triggers the collapse of a giant cloud of gas, dust, and ice.
2. As the cloud collapses, it starts to spin.
3. The spinning motion forms a disk.
4. A star forms in the middle and planets form in the disk.

▲ The first stars appeared about 100 million years after the Big Bang.

Star DEATH

Although stars appear to be constant and unchanging from century to century, they don't last forever. All the time they are shining, stars are using up fuel. When this fuel runs out, the stars die, causing some of the most extreme explosions in the Universe.

1. Red giant

When a star runs out of fuel, it swells to hundreds of times its original size, forming a red giant. The expanding outer layers of the star cool, making it look red. In about 5 billion years, the Sun will become a red giant, huge enough to swallow Mercury and Venus. The largest red giants are called red supergiants, and are up to 1,500 times bigger than the Sun.

▼ Red giants are stars that have used up all the hydrogen in their core.

THE RED GIANT SUN WILL BE UP TO 200 TIMES BIGGER THAN THE SUN TODAY.

2. White dwarf

A red giant's core eventually loses its grip on its outer layers, which drift into space. The layers form a huge shell of gas called a planetary nebula with a white dwarf, a tiny remnant of the original star, in the middle. A white dwarf cannot produce enough heat to survive, so gradually cools and dies.

▲ A giant ring of gas, a planetary nebula, surrounds a dying star.

3. Supernova

The most massive stars end their days in a violent explosion called a supernova. The star's core collapses so fast that it blasts the outer layers away. Gas rushes outward in all directions, making a glowing shell. A tiny, hot star is left in the center of the shell. A supernova can shine more brightly than a whole galaxy. After a few weeks, it fades and disappears.

4. Neutron star

After a supernova, the core that is left behind collapses to form a dense object called a neutron star. A typical neutron star is more massive than the Sun, but so dense that it is 60,000 times smaller than the Sun. A Boeing 747 squashed to the same density as a neutron star would be the size of a grain of sand!

▲ A quasar is a black hole surrounded by a disk. It is the brightest object in the Universe.

▼ A supernova blasts out gas into space in all directions.

▼ A neutron star is made of neutrons, particles of matter with no electrical charge that are normally found in atomic nuclei.

5. Black hole

A massive star continues to collapse beyond the neutron star stage, becoming a black hole. This region in space becomes so dense with such powerful gravity that nothing, not even light, can escape. It sucks in nearby stars and nebulae. Most galaxies have a supermassive black hole at their center. The black hole at the center of the Milky Way is as massive as 4.3 million Suns.

EYE IN the Sky

Some of the energy given out by stars and galaxies is blocked by Earth's atmosphere, so doesn't reach telescopes on the surface. To study this energy, telescopes and other instruments are launched into space and stay active for ten years or more.

SPECTRUM STUDY

Most of the electromagnetic spectrum does not pass through Earth's atmosphere—if any gets through, it is distorted by the atmosphere. Visible light and some radio waves reach the ground. Gamma rays, X-rays, most ultraviolet light, most infrared rays, and long radio waves can only be studied by instruments in space.

▼ Chandra studies X-rays coming from the hottest parts of the Universe.

▲ Fermi is a scientific satellite carrying a telescope that scans the Universe for gamma rays.

High-energy explorer

The Fermi Gamma-ray Space Telescope was launched in 2008 to study high-energy rays from space. These rays come from strange objects such as massive black holes and pulsars. Pulsars are spinning neutron stars that send out beams of energy. Fermi discovered new pulsars and saw high-energy explosions called gamma-ray bursts. It is designed to work in space for up to ten years.

X-ray search

The Chandra X-ray Observatory has been searching for X-rays in space since 1999. At 45 ft (14 m) long, it was the biggest satellite ever launched by a Space Shuttle. Chandra has discovered X-rays coming from black holes and pulsars. It also found new stars that had never been seen before. Some of the objects it studies are so far away that light and X-rays from them have taken 10 billion years to reach our Solar System.

ELECTROMAGNETIC ENERGY

GAMMA RAY   **X-RAY**   **ULTRAVIOLET**

The Big Four

Between 1990 and 2003, NASA's Great Observatories Program launched four powerful space telescopes. Each one studied a different part of the electromagnetic spectrum. The Hubble Space Telescope was first, working mainly with visible light. It made many major discoveries, including capturing the moment Shoemaker-Levy 9 comet collided with Jupiter in 1994. It was followed by the Compton Gamma Ray Observatory and then the Chandra X-ray Observatory. The last was the Spitzer Space Telescope, working at infrared wavelengths.

▼ The Spitzer infrared space telescope had to be super-cold to work. Liquid helium chilled it to −449°F (−267°C).

▲ The 7,300-lb (3,300-kg) Herschel Space Telescope was designed to study the coldest and dustiest objects in space.

▼ The Hubble Space Telescope has been taking spectacular photographs of stars and galaxies since 1990.

Herschel's discoveries

In 2009, the European Space Agency launched the Herschel Space Observatory. It made important discoveries about the process of star formation and the evolution of galaxies. It found enough water vapor around one young star to fill thousands of oceans, leading scientists to believe that water-covered planets may be common in the Universe. Its mission ended in 2013 when the liquid helium that cooled the telescope ran out.

Future launch

The James Webb Space Telescope is being built as a successor to the Hubble Space Telescope and will be launched in 2018. It will work mainly at infrared wavelengths, studying the history of our Universe, from the Big Bang to the evolution of the Solar System.

▲ The James Webb Space Telescope will search for new planetary systems that are forming now.

VISIBLE   INFRARED   MICROWAVE   RADIO

EXPLORING
the Universe

The Universe is so vast that most of it is too far away to reach with spacecraft. Instead, scientists use powerful telescopes to explore and observe galaxies, distant planets, and outer space objects. The largest telescopes are the most effective, creating detailed images.

STAR STUDIES
Until the 20th century, astronomers studied only the light given out by stars and galaxies. However, this is just a fraction of the radiation they emit. By studying stars a other wavelengths—such as radio, X-ray, ultraviolet, and infrared—astronomers receive more information about what' happening inside stars and galaxies, and in the space around them.

▼ The five HESS telescopes have found many new gamma ray sources in the Milky Way.

Spotting gamma rays
The High Energy Stereoscopic System (HESS) looks for gamma rays in a clever way. Earth's atmosphere blocks gamma rays from space, but as the rays dive into the atmosphere and collide with atoms, they produce flashes of light called Cerenkov radiation. Five HESS telescopes in Namibia, Africa, look at the sky from different angles to spot this telltale light.

Observatory up high
Earth's atmosphere bends starlight and causes stars to twinkle, which makes it difficult for optical telescopes to produce sharp images. One answer is to build telescopes, such as the W.M. Keck Observatory, on mountaintops where they are above most of the atmosphere. The dark skies, low humidity, and high altitude at the summit of Mauna Kea in Hawaii make it an ideal location for astronomical telescopes.

ELECTROMAGNETIC ENERGY

GAMMA RAY　　　　**X-RAY**　　　　**ULTRAVIOLET**

◄ The orange areas are clouds of hot gas on either side of a galaxy. They are invisible to ordinary telescopes, but radio telescopes reveal them.

Building the SKA

While optical telescopes use light to create images, radio telescopes use radio waves. To study radiation in the most remote parts of the Universe, astronomers need an enormous radio telescope—so they are building the biggest yet. The Square Kilometre Array (SKA) will combine radio signals from thousands of smaller antennae over an area of 0.4 sq mi (one square kilometer).

CARMA

The Combined Array for Research in Millimeter-wave Astronomy (CARMA) is a group of telescopes that study radio waves given out by cold gas and dust in space. The information collected by the 23 telescopes is combined to form detailed images. The Array has been built 7,200 ft (2,200 m) up in the Inyo Mountains, California, U.S., where the thin, dry air is perfect for receiving radio waves from space.

▼ The CARMA telescopes study the clouds of gas and dust in other galaxies where new stars are born.

▼ The summit of Mauna Kea is home to a dozen astronomical telescopes.

▼ The Square Kilometre Array is being built across two sites in Australia and South Africa.

VISIBLE　　**INFRARED**　　**MICROWAVE**　　**RADIO**

EXOPLANET
Lottery

KEPLER 22b

For centuries, astronomers believed that other stars in the Universe had their own planets—just like the Sun in the Solar System—but they could not prove it. Then in 1992 the first "extrasolar planet," or exoplanet, was discovered. Several thousand exoplanets have now been found.

KEPLER 62e

SUPER-EARTH

The first exoplanets to be found were bigger than Jupiter. As technology improved, smaller exoplanets could be detected. Exoplanets that are bigger than Earth but smaller than gas giants are called super-Earths. The first super-Earth orbiting a Sunlike star, called 55 Cancri e, was found in 2004. Kepler-22b, a super-Earth discovered in 2011, is bigger than Earth but smaller than Neptune.

HABITABLE WORLDS

The list of habitable planets is growing and recent discoveries include Kepler-62e. Known as Goldilocks planets, they lie within their star's Habitable Zone, or Goldilocks Zone—just the right distance from the star for life to exist. Scientists believe that 40 billion stars in our galaxy are similar to the Sun and there may be 8.8 billion Earth-sized planets. There is a chance that these planets may harbor life and could be colonized by humans in the distant future.

PLANET-HUNTING
SPACECRAFT

▶ The Kepler spacecraft has been hunting for planets since 2009. Its mission is expected to last until 2016.

Many of the exoplanets found so far were named after the spacecraft that discovered them, called Kepler. The number in the planet's name identifies the star and the letter identifies the planet. For example, Kepler-22b is the second planet orbiting a star called Kepler-22. The Kepler spacecraft monitors more than 100,000 stars simultaneously, detecting tiny changes in brightness due to planets that are orbiting them.

KEPLER 20f

TOO HOT FOR LIFE

The first Earth-sized exoplanet orbiting a Sunlike star was discovered in 2011. The planet, called Kepler-20e, is a little smaller than Earth. It orbits too close to its star to have liquid water on its surface. Another planet in the same system, Kepler-20f, orbits a bit further away from the star, but its surface temperature is still too high for liquid water to exist.

LUCKY DIP

Exoplanets are so far away that the only way to find them is to look for their effect on their host star. As a planet passes in front of a star, the star's brightness dips a little. Spacecraft can measure this dip and detect the planet.

▼ A planet passing in front of a star dims the brightness by just 0.01 percent.

KEPLER 20e

EXTREMELY DANGEROUS

WANTED!

SIZZLING SUN

The Sun is the nearest star to Earth and provides just the right amount of light and warmth to sustain life.

It looks like a small, yellow disk, but it's actually a gigantic ball of superhot gases—a form of matter called plasma. Magnetic storms and violent outbursts of energy rage across its surface.

DISTINGUISHING FEATURES

1 Iron at a temperature of 18 million°F (10 million°C) or more gives out radiation. This causes explosions called solar flares on the Sun's surface.

2 Helium emits radiation that shows what's happening in the Sun's chromosphere, which is 1,240 mi (2,000 km) below the surface.

3 This ultraviolet image shows activity in the Sun's chromosphere and corona (outer atmosphere).

4 Radiation from iron at one million°F (600,000°C) reveals activity in the Sun's outer atmosphere called the corona.

5 A magnetic map of the Sun shows up details of its magnetic field.

6 Radiation from iron at 11 million°F (6 million°C) shows how solar flares affect the corona.

7 A visible light image of the Sun shows a layer called the photosphere—the surface that we can see.

8 This map of the Sun, called a dopplergram, shows gas rising to the surface and sinking again.

9 Magnetically active regions of the corona are revealed by iron at 4.5 million°F (2.5 million°C).

10 Radiation from iron at up to 36 million°F (20 million°C) shows hot regions of the corona.

SPITTING MAD!

The surface of the Sun throws out long, curling tongues of gas, called prominences. They usually form in about a day and last for several weeks. The biggest loop ever recorded was 500,000 mi (800,000 km) long. Usually, the gas falls back onto the Sun, but sometimes it is thrown out into space—and could reach Earth.

▲ Prominences are loops of cooler hydrogen gas that are held in place by the Sun's magnetic field.

SPOTTY SURFACE

Dark spots called sunspots often appear on the Sun's surface. They last for a week or two and then disappear again. They are caused by regions of intense magnetism, which stop hot gas rising to the surface. They look dark because they are cooler than the rest of the Sun. Sunspot activity rises and falls on an 11-year cycle.

▲ The biggest sunspots are more than six times the size of Earth.

BRIGHT LIGHTS IN THE SKY

A shimmering glow called an aurora often appears in the sky near Earth's North and South poles. It's caused by a stream of particles called the solar wind that flies out of the Sun at up to 500 mi/sec (800 km/sec). The particles dive into the atmosphere near the poles and collide with gas atoms, which give out light and create the aurora.

▲ The Northern Lights occur in the Arctic region. The Southern Lights appear over the Antarctic.

SOLAR System

Earth—the only planet in the Universe known to harbor life.

Mars—the red planet is named after the Roman god of war.

The Solar System is the Sun and everything that surrounds it, from planets to asteroids. Measuring about 4 light-years across, the vast system of planets, moons, and other bodies is held together by gravity.

Uranus—the first planet to be discovered in modern times by using a telescope.

Sun—the superhot star at the center of the Solar System.

THE ROUND TRIP

The planets travel in elliptical orbits in the same direction as the Sun rotates. They also rotate in the same direction as the Sun, with the exception of Venus and Uranus. Venus rotates in the opposite direction to the other planets. Uranus lies on its side. Their differing rotation was probably caused by massive collisions with other bodies while the planets were forming.

ASTRONOMICAL UNITS

Earth orbits the Sun at a distance of nearly 93 million mi (150 million km), also known as 1 Astronomical Unit. The outermost planet, Neptune, orbits at a distance of 30 Astronomical Units from the Sun. The immense force of the Sun's gravity reaches out to a distance of about 2 light-years, or more than 126,000 Astronomical Units.

▶ The four planets closest to the Sun are small and rocky. The four planets furthest from the Sun are gas giants.

Mercury—the innermost planet of the Solar System, which is also the smallest.

Jupiter—the Solar System's largest planet and the first of the four gas giants.

Venus—the second planet from the Sun and the closest planet to Earth.

Neptune—the eighth Solar System planet and the most distant from the Sun.

Saturn—the second largest planet in the Solar System is well known for the rings that encircle it.

SOLAR SYSTEM DISCOVERIES

1610 Galileo Galilei discovered Jupiter's four biggest moons, now known as the Galilean moons. He also found Saturn's rings, but didn't know what they were.

1655 Giovanni Domenico Cassini discovered Jupiter's storm, the Great Red Spot. Christiaan Huygens discovered Titan, Saturn's largest moon.

1781 The planet Uranus was discovered by William Herschel.

1846 The planet Neptune was discovered by Urbain Le Verrier and Johann Gottfried Galle.

1930 Pluto was discovered by Clyde Tombaugh and named the Solar System's ninth planet.

1958 The Explorer 1 satellite discovered layers of charged particles, called the Van Allen radiation belt, around Earth.

1972 The Mariner 9 spacecraft discovered dry riverbeds, the Solar System's biggest volcano—Olympus Mons—and giant canyons on Mars.

1992 The Kuiper Belt, a region of icy bodies beyond the furthest planet, is discovered.

2005 The dwarf planet Eris was discovered. The Huygens mini-probe landed on Saturn's moon, Titan, and sent back the first photographs of its surface.

WANDERING STARS

People have studied the Solar System for thousands of years. Before telescopes were invented, astronomers could see six planets—Earth, Mercury, Venus, Mars, Jupiter, and Saturn. They were called planets from Greek words meaning "wandering stars" because of the way they move across the sky.

The ROCKIES

The four planets closest to the Sun are made of rock and each has an iron core. They have the same internal structure as Earth—made of metals and silicate rock—so they are known as terrestrial (Earthlike) planets.

Hothouse world

Slightly smaller than Earth, Venus is hidden under a thick atmosphere of carbon dioxide and sulfuric acid clouds. This atmosphere traps heat from the Sun, making Venus the Solar System's hottest planet. Its surface is covered with hundreds of volcanoes and the surface pressure on Venus is 92 times that on Earth. Venus is visible from Earth near the Sun just before sunrise and after sunset, so it is also known as the morning star or evening star.

Scorched rock

Mercury is the closest planet to the Sun, but it is not the hottest because it lacks a thick atmosphere, which would trap the heat. The smallest planet, it has a dusty surface and is covered with craters. One side of Mercury is roasted by the Sun, while the other side is frozen. This gives Mercury the greatest difference in night and day temperatures, from −280°F to 800°F (−173°C to 427°C).

Mercury
Diameter: 3,030 mi (4,876 km)
Distance from the Sun:
36 million mi (58 million km)
Time to spin once: 59 days
Time to orbit the Sun: 88 days
Average temperature: 332°F (167°C)
Moons: 0

Venus
Diameter: 7,521 mi (12,104 km)
Distance from the Sun:
67 million mi (108 million km)
Time to spin once: 243 days
Time to orbit the Sun: 225 days
Average temperature: 867°F (464°C)
Moons: 0

Home planet

Earth is the biggest of the terrestrial planets. It is the only planet known to have liquid water on its surface. The water, warmth from the Sun, and oxygen-rich atmosphere provide ideal conditions for sustaining life. Earth's surface is a thin crust of rock, on top of a layer of rock called the mantle. Below the mantle, in the middle of the planet, there is a core made of solid iron, with liquid iron around it.

The red planet

Mars is half the size of Earth and surrounded by a thin carbon dioxide atmosphere. It once had oceans and rivers, but they have now disappeared. The water probably evaporated into the thin atmosphere. The only water on Mars today is in the form of ice in its polar caps and under the surface. The red color of Mars comes from iron oxide, the same substance that makes rust look red.

Mars
Diameter: 4,212 mi (6,779 km)
Distance from the Sun:
142 million mi (228 million km)
Time to spin once: 24.6 hours
Time to orbit the Sun: 687 days
Average temperature: -85°F (-65°C)
Moons: 2

Earth
Diameter: 7,916 mi (12,742 km)
Distance from the Sun:
93 million mi (150 million km)
Time to spin once: 23.9 hours
Time to orbit the Sun: 365.2 days
Average temperature: 59°F (15°C)
Moons: 1

TRANSITS OF VENUS

Venus is closer to the Sun than Earth. Occasionally, Venus passes directly between the Sun and Earth. The distant planet looks like a small, black dot crossing the bright disk of the Sun. Hundreds of years ago, scientists used these transits of Venus to calculate the size of the Solar System. The last transit was in June 2012, and there will not be another until 2117.

EARTH'S MOON

Dominating the night sky, the Moon travels through space with Earth, making one orbit of the planet every 27 days. Apart from Earth, it is the only other space object that people have set foot on—but we still have a lot to learn about it.

▼ The protoplanet that crashed into Earth is called Theia, after an ancient Greek goddess. It was completely destroyed.

6

▼ The Sun's atmosphere becomes visible when the Moon blots out the Sun during a total solar eclipse.

CRASH! BANG!

The Moon is thought to have formed when Earth collided with a Mars-sized protoplanet, causing material to be blasted out of Earth's surface. Some of the rock thrown out began to orbit around Earth. Eventually it came together to form the Moon. This giant collision happened about 4.5 billion years ago. It is the biggest impact in Earth's history.

INCREDIBLE ECLIPSES

As the Moon orbits Earth, and Earth orbits the Sun, all three occasionally line up. If the Moon passes between Earth and the Sun, the result is a solar eclipse. The Moon blots out part or all of the Sun, leaving a ring of light. If Earth passes between the Sun and Moon, the result is a lunar eclipse. Light from the Sun leaks around Earth through its atmosphere, turning the Moon red.

▼ Moon-bases will use lunar soil, crater walls, or deep caves to protect themselves from solar radiation.

BYE BYE MOON!

The Moon is slowly drifting away from Earth at a rate of 1.48 in (3.78 cm) a year. When the Moon formed, it was only 14,000 mi (22,500 km) away and a day on Earth was only five hours long. As the Moon receded, it made Earth spin more slowly, resulting in the 24-hour day that we have now. The Moon is now 238,850 mi (384,400 km) from Earth.

LUNAR COLONIES

Moon-bases have been the stuff of science fiction for decades, but several countries are now talking about sending astronauts to the Moon for the first time since the last Apollo mission in 1972. Instead of living on the surface, they could set up home in large tunnels and caves that have been discovered by space probes. Living underground would protect astronauts from dangerous solar radiation.

▲ The distance between Earth and the Moon is measured by firing a laser at reflectors left on the Moon by the Apollo astronauts.

▼ A supermoon can look up to 15 percent bigger and 20 percent brighter than usual.

WATER ON THE MOON

Some scientists think there could be water on the Moon. It could exist as ice in the permanent shadow of craters near the poles. In 2009, India's Chandrayaan-1 probe found more than 40 permanently dark craters near the Moon's north pole. In the same year, NASA's LCROSS probe crashed a rocket into the Moon's surface and analysed the plume of material thrown up. It found evidence of water.

▼ The LCROSS space probe follows its Centaur rocket on a collision course with the Moon as it searches for water.

GIANT MOON

A supermoon occurs when the Moon's elliptical orbit causes it to come close to Earth. If it is closer to Earth at full Moon, the whole disk of the Moon looks bigger and brighter. It can happen during a new Moon too, but the Moon is then in shadow and invisible.

MEGA STUDIOS PRESENTS

LIFE ON MARS

MARINER 9 WAS THE FIRST SPACECRAFT TO ORBIT ANOTHER PLANET.

As Mars is the most Earthlike planet in the Solar System, it has always been the focus of the search for life. However, the first spacecraft to visit Mars found a dry, dusty world with no signs of life. Scientists haven't given up and the search is still on.

A MUST-SEE
★ ★ ★ ★ ★

ASTRONAUTS ON MARS

Plans for manned space missions to Mars have been made since the 1950s, but astronauts have not yet set foot on the red planet. However, Russia, America, China, and several privately funded spaceflight organizations have announced plans to send astronauts to Mars before 2040. A space voyage to Mars would be a daunting prospect because the first Martian explorers could be away from Earth for 2–3 years.

WILD WEATHER

Mars has a thinner atmosphere than Earth, so it's colder. The nighttime temperature near the poles can plunge to −195°F (−125°C). Near the equator, rovers have recorded temperatures higher than 86°F (30°C). Near the polar ice caps, snowstorms occur in winter and duststorms take place during summer.

▲ This dust storm on the surface of Mars was spotted by the Mars Reconnaissance Orbiter spacecraft in 2006.

MEGA STUDIOS AND RED PLANET PRESENT A DAVID JONES FILM "LIFE ON MARS" STARRING HERBERT WELLS AND MANFRED STEINER WRITTEN AND DIRECTED BY DAVID JONES

TERRAFORMING MARS

Making a planet more Earthlike is called "terraforming." Some scientists think it might be possible to change Mars into a planet that humans could live on without having to wear spacesuits. Melting the ice caps to release carbon dioxide, or sending large amounts of ammonia or methane from Earth to Mars would give Mars a thicker, warmer atmosphere. Then green plants could be grown, adding oxygen through the process of photosynthesis.

◀ In the distant future, a terraformed Mars might look like Earth, with water and green plants.

ROCK LIFE

In 1996, scientists announced that they had found evidence of past life on Mars in a meteorite. The meteorite, called ALH 84001, was collected in Antarctica in 1984 and contained microscopic fossils. However, other scientists argued that the structures were more likely the result of non-biological processes. Tests failed to settle the matter.

▼ Wormlike structures in the ALH 84001 Martian meteorite could be fossilized bacteria that once lived on Mars.

THE SEARCH FOR LIFE

Orbiting spacecraft, landers, and rovers have been searching for signs of life on Mars since the Mariner 9 mission in 1971. The red planet may have supported life in the past because Mars was once warmer and wetter. However, no evidence of past or present life has been found so far.

▼ The Curiosity rover has been exploring Mars since August 2012. One of its tasks is to find out if its landing site might have supported life in the past.

GAS Giants

Beyond Mars there are four giant planets known as the Jovian planets, after Jupiter. They are almost entirely made of gas, with rocky centers surrounded by liquid. Astronauts will never set foot on them because they don't have a solid surface, but spacecraft have been sent to explore them in detail.

Giant of giants

Jupiter is the largest planet in the Solar System—2.5 times the mass of all the other planets added together. It is made mainly of hydrogen and helium—the same elements as stars—so if it were 70 times more massive, it would have become a star. Underneath its atmosphere, the gas is under so much pressure that it changes to liquid. Deeper still, it behaves like metal. At the center of the planet, there is a solid core made of rock.

Jupiter
Diameter: 86,881 mi (139,822 km)
Distance from the Sun:
484 million mi (779 million km)
Time to spin once: 9.9 hours
Time to orbit the Sun: 11.9 years
Average temperature: -166°F (-110°C)
Moons: 67

JUPITER'S GREAT RED SPOT
IS A HURRICANE-LIKE
STORM THAT'S 2.5 TIMES
BIGGER THAN EARTH.

Furthest away

The outermost planet in the Solar System, Neptune's chemical makeup is similar to that of Uranus. Its blue color is caused by methane gas in its atmosphere. Enormous, dark, Earth-sized storms have appeared in its atmosphere from time to time, but disappear after a few years. The fastest winds in the Solar System have been detected on Neptune, with a top speed of 1,500 mph (2,400 km/h).

Neptune
Diameter: 30,598 mi (49,243 km)
Distance from the Sun:
2,793 million mi (4,495 million km)
Time to spin once: 16.1 hours
Time to orbit the Sun: 163 years
Average temperature: –328°F (–200°C)
Moons: 14

Ringed planet

The Solar System's second-largest planet, Saturn, is famous for its bright rings made of water-ice. The other three gas giants have rings too, but they're thin, dark, and dusty. Like Jupiter, Saturn is made mostly of hydrogen and helium. Superfast winds and heat rising from the planet's interior cause hazy yellow bands in its atmosphere.

Saturn
Diameter: 74,998 mi (120,698 km)
Distance from the Sun:
891 million mi (1,434 million km)
Time to spin once: 10.7 hours
Time to orbit the Sun: 29.4 years
Average temperature: –220°F (–140°C)
Moons: 62

Tilted spin

In addition to hydrogen and helium, Uranus contains water, ammonia, and methane gas. Methane in its atmosphere gives the planet its blue-green color. As it orbits the Sun, tilted on its side, one pole receives continuous sunlight for 42 years, and then the other pole faces the Sun for the next 42 years.

Uranus
Diameter: 31,518 mi (50,724 km)
Distance from the Sun:
1,785 million mi (2,873 million km)
Time to spin once: 17.2 hours
Time to orbit the Sun: 83.7 years
Average temperature: –320°F (–195°C)
Moons: 27

MANY *Moons*

More than 160 moons orbit the planets in the Solar System. As technology improves, more moons are discovered. The number of known moons has nearly doubled since 2003. Most of them are tiny worlds orbiting the gas giants, but the biggest, Jupiter's moon Ganymede, is bigger than Mercury.

TITAN, DENSE WITH RIVERS OF METHANE

One of Saturn's moons, Titan, is the only moon with a dense atmosphere and the only body in the Solar System, apart from Earth, to have liquid on its surface. The Cassini spacecraft dropped the *Huygens* probe on Titan. It photographed the surface, but the rivers and lakes it found aren't filled with water—they're full of liquid methane.

SHEPHERD MOONS, DUSTY AND CRATERED

Some of Saturn's rings have defined edges because moons are orbiting nearby or inside gaps between the rings. They are called shepherd moons because their gravity keeps the ring particles together like a shepherd herds a flock of sheep. Any particles that stray out of the ring are either deflected back into the ring or attracted onto the moon by its gravity.

EUROPA, WATERY WITH A THICK, ICY SURFACE

One of Jupiter's moons, Europa, is covered with ice that might be floating on a water ocean up to 60 mi (100 km) deep. It is thought that this ocean could harbor life. To protect it from bacterial contamination, the Galileo space probe that explored Jupiter and its moons was deliberately sent into Jupiter's atmosphere to burn up.

TRITON, WITH BURSTS OF LIQUID NITROGEN

Many moons that orbit the outer planets are asteroids that were captured by the planets. One sign of this is if the moon orbits in the opposite direction to other moons—Triton, Neptune's largest moon, does this. Triton is so cold that it has ice volcanoes shooting out a mixture of liquid nitrogen, methane, and dust.

MIRANDA, ICY WITH CRACKS AND CANYONS

Uranus' small moon, Miranda, is covered with a strange patchwork pattern of canyons, grooves, and cracks. It may be that this tiny world was smashed apart by a collision long ago and then the parts came together again in orbit. Scientists think its surface is made mostly of ice.

GANYMEDE, WITH A THICK LAYER OF ICE

Jupiter's moon Ganymede is the biggest moon in the Solar System, larger than Mercury. It is thought to be covered with a deep layer of ice up to 500 mi (800 km) thick. Discovered in 1610, Ganymede and three other large moons of Jupiter were the first moons ever seen orbiting another planet.

DWARFS
in Space

Countless millions of small worlds made of rock and ice orbit the Sun between the planets and far beyond them. Some of these worlds are nearly as big as planets, so they are called dwarf planets. Many of them are found in the Kuiper Belt.

EX-PLANET

In 1930, U.S. astronomer Clyde Tombaugh discovered the Solar System's ninth planet, Pluto. In 2005, another distant planet, named Eris, was found. At first, it was hailed as the Solar System's tenth planet. When astronomers realized that many more of these small worlds are likely to be discovered, they decided to call them dwarf planets.

▲ The New Horizons space probe will fly past Pluto in 2015 and then carry on into the Kuiper Belt.

COMPARING THE BELTS

The Kuiper Belt is like the Asteroid Belt but further away and far bigger. It lies beyond Neptune's orbit, is about twice the size of the Solar System, and consists of lots of cometlike objects. The Asteroid Belt extends from Mars to Jupiter. Although, the Kuiper Belt is 20 times wider then the Asteroid Belt and 200 times more massive, it is so far away that we can see very little of it.

▼ The Kuiper Belt is a disk-shaped region that extends from Neptune's orbit to 4.6 billion mi (7.4 billion km) from the Sun.

Asteroid Belt

Kuiper Belt

EGG PLANET

Dwarf planet Haumea has a reddish spot on its surface. Calculations based on the way it reflects light suggest that Haumea has a stretched elliptical shape, with its length twice as long as its width. Its strange shape may be caused by its fast rotation—it spins once every four hours, possibly due to a collision with something in the past.

▲ Haumea is very dense, so it probably contains more rock and less ice than other Kuiper Belt objects.

▲ Eris was discovered in 2005 and named as a dwarf planet on September 13, 2006.

WARRIOR PRINCESS

Dwarf planet Eris orbits the Sun three times further out than Pluto and has a tiny moon called Dysnomia. It was first named after a television series, *Xena: Warrior Princess*. Later, it was given its official name of Eris, after the Greek god of strife, chaos, and discord.

▲ Makemake is so small and far away that, even through the most powerful telescope, it is a tiny, blurred image.

FAR, FAR AWAY

The dwarf planet Makemake was discovered on March 31, 2005, by astronomers at the Palomar Observatory in the U.S. It was named after a god worshipped by the Easter Island people, because it was discovered at Easter. It is so far away that it takes nearly 310 years to orbit the Sun.

▼ The dwarf planet Ceres may have a deep layer of ice under its thin, dusty crust.

THE BIGGEST ASTEROID

At 590 mi (950 km) across, Ceres is the biggest asteroid in the Asteroid Belt. When it was discovered in 1801, it was thought to be a comet. When smaller similar objects were found, the word "asteroid" was invented to describe them. Finally, when Pluto was reclassified as a dwarf planet, Ceres became a dwarf planet too. The Dawn probe, launched in 2007, visited the giant asteroid Vesta in 2011, on the way to explore Ceres.

TO THE
EXTREMES

The Solar System is a place of extremes and strange phenomena. Sulfur-spewing volcanoes, comet storms, and mysterious glows in a planet's atmosphere continually surprise and amaze scientists. The more they study the Solar System, the more surprises they find.

▼ Io's volcanic activity is driven by heat caused by the gravitational pull of Jupiter and its other moons.

VOLCANO WORLD

Io, one of Jupiter's moons, is the most geologically active object in the Solar System. This tiny world is covered with hundreds of active volcanoes. The yellow, orange, and black colors on its surface are sulfur at different temperatures. White patches are sulfur dioxide frost. Active volcanoes are found in only two other places in the Solar System—Earth and Enceladus, one of Saturn's moons.

Aurorae are named after the Roman goddess of the dawn.

Polar lights

The poles of Jupiter and Saturn are sometimes lit up by shimmering rings of light called aurorae, fuelled by particles flying off their moons. In images taken by the Hubble Space Telescope, the aurorae appear blue because of the ultraviolet camera, but they are actually red and purple. The color comes from excited hydrogen molecules.

▲ Saturn's aurorae shimmer and glow up to 600 mi (1,000 km) above its clouds.

й Ламзин

тель директора астрономического
та им. Штенберга МГУ

МВД РФ

Near-Earth Objects

Countless comets and asteroids fly through the Solar System. Occasionally, their orbits are affected by the gravitational pull of other planets and moons, bringing them close to Earth. Some near-Earth Objects pose a danger to Earth, so thousands of orbits are closely monitored. Small, stony asteroids hit Earth every year, but major impacts only occur every few thousand years.

◀ On February 13, 2013, a near-Earth asteroid dived into our atmosphere and exploded over Chelyabink in Russia.

EXTREME TEMPERATURES

Temperatures in the Solar System range from 27 million°F (15 million°C) at the center of the Sun to just a few degrees above absolute zero (−459°F or −273°C) in the Oort Cloud on the outermost fringes of the Solar System.

❝ A sungrazing comet called Ikeya-Seki came within 280,000 mi (450,000 km) of the Sun in 1965 and survived! ❞

▲ A long-tailed sungrazing comet (left) sweeps past the Sun, seen by the SOHO space probe.

Icy storm

In December 2011, a comet storm began in space. In ten days, 25 comets, known as sungrazers, were seen diving into the Sun. Recorded by the Solar and Heliospheric Observatory (SOHO) space probe, a comet storm like this had never been seen before. Since its launch in 1995, SOHO has discovered more than 2,400 comets while monitoring the Sun.

INDEX

◄ When explosives are set off, by applying heat or friction, they instantly produce intense heat and a large volume of expanding gas.

INDEX

Entries in **bold** refer to main subject entries; entries in *italics* refer to illustrations.

ACKNOWLEDGMENTS

The publishers would like to thank the following sources for the use of their photographs:

KEY
A/AL=Alamy, B=Bridgeman, CO=Corbis, D=Dreamstime, F=Fotolia, FLPA=Frank Lane Picture Agency, GI=Getty Images, GW=Glow Images, IS=istockphoto.com, MP=Minden Pictures, N=Newscom, NG=National Geographic Creative, NPL=Nature Picture Library, P=Photoshot, PL=Photolibrary, R=Reuters, RF=Rex Features, S=Shutterstock, SJC=Stuart Jackson-Carter, SPL=Science Photo Library, SS=Superstock, TF=Topfoto

t=top, a=above, b=bottom/below, c=center, l=left, r=right, f=far, m=main, bg=background

FRONT COVER Eric Boucher/S, SPINE amy27feb/S, BACK COVER Andrea Danti/S, Mark Scott/S, Sebastian Kaulitzki/S, Tony Hallas/NASA, PRELIMS 1 F, 2–3 RTimages/S, 4 Dmitri Melnik/S, 5 SNEHIT/S, iurii/S

INCREDIBLE SCIENCE 6–7 A 8–9 David Scharf/SPL 8(tl) Pedro Nogueira/S, (tr) NASA-JPL, (bl) Lane V. Erickson/S, (b, l–r) Top Photo Group/RF 9(tl) Pedro Nogueira/S, (bl) James Balog/Aurora Photos/Corbis, (r, t–b) oku/S, David Arts/S, Dmitri Melnik/S, Sergey Kamshylin/S, Andrey Burmakin/S, (frame) Phase4Photography/S 10–11(m) NASA/GI, (b) Joseph C Dovala/P 10(l) Edward Kinsman/SPL, (c) Abel Tumik/S, (b, panel) Matthias Pahl/S, (b, chain) Henry Nowick/S, (r) Phase4Photography/S 11(l) E.R.Degginger/SPL, (r, t–b) Melli/S, Vakhrushev Pavel/S, Arsgera/S, ArtmannWitte/S 12–13(bg) lolloj/S 12(m) GI, (t) Eye of Science/SPL, (bl) Nicemonkey/S, (br) Lawrence Berkeley National Laboratory/SPL 13(tl) NASA/SPL, (tr) RF, (bm) Innespace Productions/SEABREACHER, (bl) Dmitri Mihhailov/S, (br) Gwoeii/S 14–5(bg) dinadesign/S, (frame) ivn3da/S, (c) adziohiciek/S, (ice cubes) Alex Staroseltsev/S 14(tr) NASA/Science Faction/Corbis, (bl) Vitaly Raduntsev/S, (br) SPL 15(tl) Patrick Landmann/SPL, (tr) Ria Novosti/SPL, (tr, frame) Hintau Aliaksei, (bl) Diego Barucco/S, (br) Yva Momatiuk & John Eastcott/GI 16–7(bg) Zinatova Olga/S, (c) Gordan/S, (b) Sergey Mironov/S, (t) NASA-JPL 16(l) Edward Kinsman/SPL, (r) Jean-Luc & Françoise Ziegler/P 17(t) NASA-GSFC, (bl) NASA-JPL, (br) NASA/WMAP Science Team/SPL 18–9(bg, wood) Ford Photography/S, (bg, book) Valentin Agapov/S, (doodles) Bukhavets Mikhail/S, (masking tape) Studio DMM Photography, Designs & Art/S, (frames) Phase4Photography/S 18(t) NASA-MSFC, (b) NASA-JPL 19(tr) Viktar Malyshchyts/S, (r) happydancing/S 20–1(m) Tony Craddock/SPL 20(b) J.C. Revy, ISM/SPL 21 Volker Springel/Max Planck Institute for Astrophysics/SPL 22–3(bg) Kheng Guan Toh/S, (atoms) Johan Swanepoel/S, (molecules) Serdar Duran/S 22(l) Steve Gschmeissner/SPL, (tr) David McCarthy/SPL, (br) Susumu Nishinaga/SPL 23(t) Dr Gary Gaugler/SPL, (cl) Dr Linda Stannard, UCT/SPL, (cr) Omikron/SPL, (b) Jan Kaliciak/S 24(t) Eye of science/SPL, (c) Ower and Syred/SPL, (b) SPL 25(tl) Jan Hinsch/SPL, (tr) Susumu Nishinaga/SPL, (bl) Steve Gschmeissner/

SPL, (br) Astrid & Hanns-Frieder Michler/SPL 26(bg) argus/S, (m) Thierry Berrod, Mona Lisa Production/SPL, (b) Bristish Museum/Munoz-Yague/SPL 27(m) Stephen & Donna O'Meara/SPL, (tl) Jochen Tack/P, (tr) Augusto Cabral/S, (bl) Smit/S 28–9(m) Anakaopress/Look at sciences/SPL 28(b) optimarc/S 29(t) Stephen Alvarez/GI, (c) Carsten Peter/GI, (b) Jeff Rotman/NPL 30–9(t) shelbysupercars.com, (b) David J. Cross/P 30 GI 31 NASA/SPL 32(bg, pink) Panos Karapanagiotis/S, (bg, writing) Inga Nielsen/S, (tl) National Library of Medicine/SPL, (tr) Dmitrijs Bindemanis/S, (cl) Library of Congress/digital version by Science Faction, (bl) Bettmann/Corbis, (br) Dominik Michálek/S 33(tl) Jacqueline Abromeit, (tr) RF, (cl) Bettmann/Corbis, (bl) Graeme Dawes/S, (bc) NASA-MSFC, (br) Reuters/Corbis 34–5(m) Russell Kightley/SPL 34 NASA/ESA/STSCI/J.Kenney & E. Yale, Yale University/SPL 35 Chandra X-ray Observatory/NASA/SPL 36–7(bg) David Parker/SPL, (clockwise starting bl) Christophe Vander Eecken/Reporters/SPL, Adam Hart-Davis/SPL, Tim Wright/Corbis, optimarc/S, Sylverarts/S, Emilio Naranjo/epa/Corbis 38–9(border) gorica/S 38(tl) INSAGO/S, (cl) R-studio/S, (bl) GI 39(tl) Christophe Boisvieux/Corbis, (bl) Time & Life Pictures/GI, (r) Omikron/SPL 40–1 Jose Antonio Peñas/SPL (c) T Carrafa/Newspix/RF, (r) Anan Kaewkhammul/S

BODY SCIENCE 42–3 Segalen/Phanie/RF; 44–5 aliisik/S, Sarunyu_foto/S, aopsan/S; 44(tr) Willdidthis/S, (tr) R-studio/S; 45 Cordelia Molloy/SPL, (b) Viacheslav A. Zotov/S, (bl) vvoe/S, (br) Andrea Danti/S, (tl) Twelve/S, (tl) SeDmi/S; 46 Steve Gschmeissner/SPL, (br) SPL/GI; 47 Dr. Kessel & Dr. Kardon/Tissues & Organs/GI, (bl) Alexey Khromushin/F, (br) J.C. Revy, ISM/SPL, (t) Aaron Amat/S; 48–9 Science Picture Co/GI, Palsur/S; 48(bl) GRei/S, (bl) Linali/S; 50–1 R-studio/S, (tc) TebNad/S; 50(bl) Michal Kowalski/S, (bl) R. Bick, B. Poindexter, Ut Medical School/SPL, (br) Litvinenko Anastasia/S, (br) Olivier Le Queinec/S, (br) B Calkins/S, (cl) kedrov/S, (cr) Nixx Photography/S, (cr) Anusorn P nachol/S, (cr) Prof. P. Motta/Dept. of Anatomy/University "La Sapienza", Rome/SPL, (tl) Oleksii Natykach/S, (tl) ZoneFatal/S, (tl) wmedien/S, (tl) ojka/S, (tr) Yevgen Kotyukh/S; 51(bl) happykanppy/S, (br) Anthony DiChello/S, (cl) Scimat/SPL, (cr) nikkytok/S, (tl) Yaraz/S, (tl) Steve Gschmeissner/SPL, (tr) Volker Steger/SPL; 52–3 Sergey Panteleev/IS; 52(bl) St Bartholomew's Hospital/SPL, (br) Paul Gunning/SPL, (cr) Fedor Kondratenko/S; 53(br) SPL, (t) Dr. Richard Kessel & Dr. Randy Kardon/Tissues & Organs/Visuals Unlimited/CO; 54 Leigh Prather/S, (br) Diego Cervo/S, (cr) Mikhail/S, (cr) Bill Longcore/SPL, (l) Scientifica/GI, (tr) Ozerina Anna/S; 55 Gunnar Pippel/S, (r) Colleen Petch/Newspix/RF, (bc) Alex Staroseltsev/S, (bl) AFP/GI, (bl) Alex Varlakov/IS, (br) Martin Dohrn/SPL, (cr) Alex073/S, (tl) Eric Gevaert/S; 56–7 Neliyana Kostadinova/S, Ramon Andrade 3Dciencia/SPL; 56(br) 3d4medical.com/SPL, (l) Sebastian Kaulitzki/S, (l) Zephyr/SPL; 57(tr) Sovereign, ISM/SPL; 58–9 Medical Images, Universal Images Group/SPL; 58(bl) Sergey Furtaev/S, (cr) Steve Gschmeissner/S; 59(bl) Gunnar Pippel/S, (br) Kannanimages/S, (tl) Similar Images Preview/GI;

60–1 pio3/S, Eky Studio/S, Mark Beckwith/S; 60(bl) Pascal Goetgheluck/SPL, (tr) Suren Manvelyan/RF; 61(br) Anatomical Travelogue/SPL, (cl) Ralph C. Eagle, Jr/SPL, (cr) Omikron/SPL, (tr) guido nardacci/S; 62–3(c) Dragana Gerasimoski/S, (tc) Carolina Biological Supply Co/Visuals Unlimited, Inc/SPL; 62(bc) Dr Yorgos Nikas/SPL, (tl) Medi-Mation/GI; 63(bl) Zephyr/SPL, (br) Eugen Shevchenko/S, (tr) Simon Fraser/SPL; 64(bc) Monika Wisniewska/S, (r) Monkey Business Images/S; 65(r) Troels Graugaard/IS, (r) Yuri Arcurs/S, (bc) Kais Tolmats/IS, (tc) 4x6/IS; 66–7 Franck Boston/S, (c) Friedrich Saurer/SPL; 66(bl) Thomas Deerinck, NCMIR/SPL, (cl) Frederick R. Matzen/S, (tr) Aptyp_koK/S; 67(bc) Olga Lipatova/S, (br) Professors P.M. Motta, P.M. Andrews, K.R. Porter & J. Vial/SPL, (tr) Don Fawcett/SPL; 68–9(c) Gustoimages/GI; 68(bc) SPL/GI, (bl) ImageryMajestic/S, (cl) Steve Gschmeissner/SPL; 69(br) Netfalls–Remy Musser/S, (cl) Gustoimages/GI, (tc) Susumu Nishinaga/SPL; 70–1 blackred/IS, Skocko/S, Angela Harburn/S; 70(bl) Thierry Berrod, Mona Lisa Production/SPL, (br) Power and Syred/SPL, (t) D. Kucharski & K. Kucharska/S, (t) Ultrashock/S, (tl) Retrofile/GI; 71(bl) Francis Leroy, Biocosmos/SPL, (br) Coneyl Jay/SPL, (tr) Dr. Richard Kessel & Dr. Gene Shih, Visuals Unlimited/SPL; 72–3 Ford Photography/S, Nata-Lia/S; 72(cl) Andrew Taylor/S, (t) Falkiewicz Henryk/S, (tl) Igor Kovalchuk/S, (tr) Picsfive/S, (tr) Johanna Goodyear/S; 73(bl) discpicture/S, (tl) Marilyn Volan/S; 74–5 saicle/S; 74(l) Murdoch Ferguson/RF; 75(bl) Mark Carrel/S, (bl) Library Of Congress/SPL, (br) Dr Yorgos Nikas/SPL, (tr) Zephyr/GI, (tr) Gordan/S, (tr) SAM OGDEN/SPL; 76–7 robertlamphoto/S; 76(bl) kanate/S, (c) Sukharevskyy Dmytro (nevodka)/S, (cl) Dee Breger/SPL, (t) David Mack/SPL; 77(br) Lusoimages/S, (br) Michael W. Davidson/SPL, (cl) Paul A. Souders/CO, (tr) Nils Jorgensen/RF

WILD SCIENCE 78–9 Al Francekevich/CO, 80–1 alexwhite/S, 80–1(bg) Bobbie Sandlin/S, 80–1(bg) Elkostas/S, 80(br) Rex Features, 80(cl) N, 81(bl) MATT MEADOWS/SPL, 81(br) KAZUHIRO NOGI/AFP/GI, 81(t) NATIONAL INSTITUTE OF STANDARDS AND TECHNOLOGY (NIST)/SPL, 83 mashurov/S, 82–3 val lawless/S, 82–3 kanate/S, 82–3 nikkytok/S, 82–3(bg) Romeo/D, 82–3(c) Courtesy Everett Collection/RF, 82(br) Top Photo Group/RF, 82(cl) US NAVY/SPL, 83(b) ZUMA/RF, 83(r) kristian sekulic/S, 83(t) Andrey Bayda/S, 83(tr) Loskutnikov/S, 83(tr) 123RF, 84–5 val lawless/S, 84–5 kanate/S, 84–5(bg) S_L/S, 84(bl) Andraž Cerar/S, 84(bl) Gavran/S, 84(br) Theodore Gray/Visuals Unlimited/CO, 84(br) Triff/S, 84(cl) Philip Evans/Visuals Unlimited/CO, 84(cr) photastic/S, 84(cr) Surrphoto/S, 85(bl) HEALTH PROTECTION AGENCY/SPL, 85(br) Myotis/S, 85(br) gabor00/S, 85(br) RIA NOVOSTI/SPL, 85(cl) CHARLES D. WINTERS/SPL, 85(tl) Picsfive/S, 85(tr) CHARLES D. WINTERS/SPL, 86–7 kanate/S, 86–7(bg) Peter Dazeley/GI, 86(bl) graja/S, 86(br) Jaimie Duplass/S, 86(c) ANDREW LAMBERT PHOTOGRAPHY/SPL, 86(cl) Konstanttin/S, 86(tr) Picsfive/S, 87(b) dcb/S, 87(b) ivelly/S, 87(b) Odua Images/S, 87(cr) phototh/S, 87(cr) Picsfive/S, 87(cr) CHARLES D. WINTERS/SPL, 87(l) CHARLES D. WINTERS/SPL, 87(tr) Liveshot/S, 87(tr) inxti/S, 87(tr) Andrey_Popov/S, 88–9 Anneka/S, 88–9 Kerstin Schoene/S, 88–9 (bg) bluecrayola/S, 88(b) rangizzz/S, 88(bl) JOCHEN LUEBKE/epa/CO, 88(tr) hxdbzxy/S, 88(tr) Thinkstock, 89(bc) gabor00/S, 89(br) MICHAEL DONNE/SPL, 89(c) Christian Kober/GI, 89(t) Custom Medical Stock Photo/N, 89(t) silky/S, 89(tr) kanate/S, 90–1 val lawless/S, 90–1 kanate/S, 90–1(b) SPL, 90–1(bg) S, 90–1(t) Mark Schneider/Visuals Unlimited/CO, 90(b) Visuals Unlimited/CO, 90(bl) gabor00/S, 90(tc) Theodore Gray/Visuals Unlimited/CO, 90(tl) Theodore Gray/Visuals Unlimited/CO, 91(bl) D, 91(br) Theodore Gray,/Visuals Unlimited/CO, 91(cr) SCIENTIFICA, VISUALS UNLIMITED/SPL, 91(tc) CHARLES D. WINTERS/SPL, 91(tr) bonchan/S, 92–3 Liam Brazier, 94–5(bg) Joel Shawn/S, 94–5(bg) FuzzBones/S, 94(bl) Wolna/S, 94(bl) PASQUALE SORRENTINO/SPL, 94(br) archetype/S, 94(c) Dmitry Naumov/S, 94(c) Michal Kowalski/S, 94(tr) DAVID PARKER FOR ESA/CNES/ARIANESPACE/SPL, 95(b) DR P. MARAZZI/SPL, 95(cr) Denis Semenchenko/S, 95(cr) DU CANE MEDICAL IMAGING LTD/SPL, 95(tc) Natalia Semenchenko/S, 95(tl) AFP/GI, 95(tl) Africa Studio/S, 96–7(bg) S, 96(br) DR KEN MACDONALD/SPL, 96(c) Anette Linnea Rasmus/F, 96(c) atip/S, 96(c) photo5963/S, 96(l) rook76/S, 96(l) Stanislav V/S, 96(tr) mikeledray/S, 96(tr) Tovkach Oleg/S, 96(tr) Garsya/S, 97(b) andzhey/S, 97(bc) PHOTO RESEARCHERS, INC/SPL, 97(bl) kanate/S, 97(cl) DETLEV VAN RAVENSWAAY/SPL, 97(tl) N, 97(tl) Guy J. Sagi/S, 99(bc) Malcolm Leman/S, 98–9 Dusit/S, 98–9(b) Reinhold Leitner/S, 98–9(bg) ivosar/S, 98–9(bg) Matee Nuserm/S, 98(bc) oksana/S, 98(bl) andersphoto/S, 98(bl) Jmiks/S, 98(bl) PETER MENZEL/SPL, 98(br) Anteromite/S, 99(bl) Jim Barber/S, 99(bl) Pan Xunbin/S, 99(br) Anthonycz/S, 99(br) denirofoto/S, 99(cl) Voyagerix/S, 99(l) M.E. Mulder/S, 99(r) sabri deniz kizil/S, 99(tl) ppart/S, 99(tr) Ingrid Prats/S, 99(tr) PaintDoor/S, 99(r) stoyanh/S, 100–1 GAUTIER Stephane/SAGAPHOTO.COM/A, 100–1(b) NASA, 100(cl) Mikhail Bakunovich/S, 100(tc) Andrzej Wilusz/S, 100(tl) Luc Sesselle/S, 100(tr) Eduardo Rivero/S, 101(br) ROBERT BROOK/SPL, 101(cl) 2happy/S, 101(tr) Paul A. Souders/CO, 102–3(bg) unitypix/S, 102(bl) Danny Smythe/S, 102(c) Iaroslav Neliubov/S, 102(cl) Harry studio/S, 102(cl) Igor Iakovlev/S, 102(cr) xpixel/S, 102(tr) Claudio Divizia/S, 103(tr) John Wollwerth/S, 103(tc) Wade H. Massie/S, 103(tc) BsWei/S, 103(tc) Andrzej Tokarski/S, 103(tr) Louise Murray/RF, 103(tr) Designs Stock/S, 104–5(bg) Maglara/S, 104(bc) Andy Dean Photography/S, 104(bl) Bettmann/CO, 104(bl) Mats/S, 104(br) SSPL/GI, 104(c) Incomible/S, 104(c) Garsya/S, 104(c) ROYAL INSTITUTION OF GREAT BRITAIN/SPL, 104(cl) Dragan85/S, 104(tr) RetroClipArt/S, 104(bl) bigredlynx/S, 105(br) Everett Collection/RF, 105(c) Andrey Eremin/S, 105(c) EMILIO SEGRE VISUAL ARCHIVES/AMERICAN INSTITUTE OF PHYSICS/SPL, 105(cl) Snaprender/S, 105(cl) photosync/S, 105(cl) Kazyavka/S, 105(cl) SPL, 105(t) bigredlynx/S, 105(tc) SSPL/GI, 105(tc) Giuseppe_R/S, 105(tl) Serazetdinov/D, 106–107(c) Anest/S, 106(b) Stephen Dalton/Minden Pictures/CO, 106(t) Gl0ck/S, 106(tr) Tatiana Popova/S, 107(br) VOLKER

STEGER/SPL, 107(c) US ARMY/SPL, 107(tr) Imperial War Museum, 108–9(b) AFP/GI, 108–9(bg) Martin Capek/S, 108(bl) PETER MENZEL/SPL, 108(tl) Masekesam/S, 108(tr) kbgen/S, 108(tr) CROWN COPYRIGHT/HEALTH & SAFETY LABORATORY/SPL, 109(br) Jakelv7500/D, 109(cr) Peter Terren/RF, 109(tl) James L. Amos/CO, 109(tl) caesart/S, 109(tr) Gunnar Pippel/S, 110–11(b) B.Lallo/IBL/RF, 110–11(t) Kyodo/N, 110(bl) HEALTH PROTECTION AGENCY/ SPL, 110(cl) Yuliyan Velchev/S, 111(br) Asahi Shimbun/GI, 111(r) Icholakov/D, 111(tl) Ed Kashi/CO, 111(tl) Oksa/S, 111(tr) RIA NOVOSTI/SPL, 112–13 Steve Bonini/GI, 112–13(b) max blain/S, 112(b) jannoon/S, 112(b) gudinny/S, 112(c) TAKE 101 LTD/SPL, 112(tr) NASA/ESA/STSCI/J.HESTER & P.SCOWEN, ASU/SPL, 113(b) discpicture/S, 113(cl) Eric Boucher/S, 113(cl) NASA/JPL-CALTECH/SPL, 113(cr) MARK GARLICK/SPL, 113(tl) TONY & DAPHNE HALLAS/SPL, 113(tr) NASA/JPL-CALTECH/STSCI/SPL

EXTREME UNIVERSE 114–15 Tony Hallas/NASA, 116–17 Ford Photography/S, 116–17(c) Igor Kovalchuk/S, 116–17(b) ESA and the Planck Collaboration, 116–17(b) nuttakit/S, 116(bl) Erik Svoboda/S, 116(bl) HARALD RITSCH/SPL, 116(br) Nata-Lia/S, 116(tl) Falkiewicz Henryk/S, 116(tl) Bukhavets Mikhail/S, 116(tl) rangizzz/S, 116(tr) DR JEAN LORRE/SPL, 117(bc) Lasse Kristensen/S, 117(br) NASA, ESA, and J. Lotz, M. Mountain, A. Koekemoer, and the HFF Team(STScI), 117(br) Evgenia Sh/S, 117(cr) Kbiros/S, 117(tl) Fotolia, 117(tl) Silhouette Lover/S, 117(tl) MEHAU KULYK/SPL, 117(tr) optimarc/S, 117(tr) Tatiana Popova/S, 118–119 Peshkova/S, 118(bl) Robert Gendler/NASA, 118(br) NASA, ESA, STScI (N. Pirzkal and the HUDF Team), 118(tr) Jean-Charles Cuillandre (CFHT) & Giovanni Anselmi (Coelum Astronomia), Hawaiian Starlight/NASA, 118(tr) Descubre Foundation, Calar Alto Observatory, OAUV, DSA, V. Peris (OAUV), J. L. Lamadrid (CEFCA), J. Harvey (SSRO), S. Mazlin (SSRO), I. Rodriguez (PTeam), O. L. (PTeam), J. Conejero (PixInsight)/NASA, 118(tr) NASA, ESA, The Hubble Heritage Team, (STScI/AURA) , 119(b) ESA/Hubble & NASA, 119(bc) Kamenetskiy Konstantin/S, 119(br) bikeriderlondon/S, 119(tl) far-infrared: ESA/Herschel/PACS/SPIRE/Hill, Motte, HOBYS Key Programme Consortium; X-ray: ESA/XMM-Newton/EPIC/XMM-Newton-SOC/Boulanger, 119(tr) Paris Owl/S, 120–1 Stephen Banks/Caters News Agency, 120(b) Fotolia, 120(bl) LeonP/S, 120(bl) Horiyan/S, 120(br) Serge Brunier/NASA, 120(cl) NASA JPL, 121(r) Yarik/S, 121(b) NASA/JPL-Caltech, 121(b) Feng Yu/S, 121(t) MARK GARLICK/SPL, 122(c) EUROPEAN SPACE AGENCY/SPL, 122(r) Steve Collender/S, 122-3(bg) Lisa A/S, 122–3(b) Olga Kovalenko/S, 122(bl) ANCH/S, 122(bl) Evikka/S, 122(br) PAUL WOOTTON/SPL, 122(cl) Boris Sosnovyy/S, 122(l) HeinSchlebusch/S, 122(tc) Triff/S, 122(tl) kikka69/S, 122(tl) ROYAL OBSERVATORY, EDINBURGH/AAO/SPL, 123(r) rangizzz/S, 123(b) Hank Frentz/S, 123(bl) MARK GARLICK/SPL, 123(br) Picsfive/S, 123(l) CHRISTIAN DARKIN/SPL, 123(tr) Redsapphire/S, 124–125(b) Rob van Esch/S, 124(bl) CHRIS BUTLER/SPL, 124(br) STScI/NASA/CO, 124(tl) MARK GARLICK/SPL, 125(r) UIG via GI, 125(bc) NASA/JPL-Caltech/CO, 125(bl) NASA, ESA, Zolt Levay (STScI), 126–7(c) NASA, 126(cl) CARLOS CLARIVAN/SPL, 126(cr) DETLEV VAN RAVENSWAAY/SPL, 127(cl) NASA/Bryan Allen/CO, 127(cr) NASA/

SPL, 127(t) DAVID DUCROS, ESA/SPL, 128–9(c) SIMON FRASER/SPL, 128(cl) PATRICK DUMAS/LOOK AT SCIENCES/SPL, 129(c) Ed Darack/SuperStock/CO, 129(r) REBECCA LE MAY/epa/CO, 129(tl) NRAO/AUI/NSF/SPL, 130–1(bg) zentilia/S, 130(l) NASA/Ames/JPL-Caltech , 130(l) zentilia/S, 130(tr) NASA/SPL, 131(bl) NASA/SPL, 131(br) Artem Furman/S, 131(br) Nicemonkey/S, 131(br) DETLEV VAN RAVENSWAAY/SPL, 131(tr) LYNETTE COOK/SPL, 132–3 NASA/SDO/Goddard Space Flight Center, 132–3(bg) nuttakit/S, 132–3(bg) mexrix/S, 133(br) Atiketta Sangasaeng/S, 133(cr) NASA/SDO/AIA/HMI/Goddard Space Flight Center, 133(tr) NASA/GSFC/Solar Dynamics Observatory's AIA Instrument, 134–5 Pavel L Photo and Video/S, 134–5 Bobboz/S, 134–5(c) Triff/S, 134–5(b) Vlue/S, 134(tl) bepsy/S, 134(tl) Christophe BOISSON/S, 136(r) World History Archive/N, 136–7 UIG via GI, 136(bc) kurt G/S, 136(bl) NASA / JHU Applied Physics Lab / Carnegie Inst. Washington, 136(br) mdd/S, 137(br) NASA ESA G Bacon(STScI), 137(br) Kaspri/S, 137(l) NASA/NOAA/GSFC/Suomi NPP/VIIRS/Norman Kuring, 137(tr) DETLEV VAN RAVENSWAAY/SPL, 139 Frank Armstrong/UT-Austin, 138(c) Boris Franz/S, 138–9(bg) Claudio Divizia/S, 138(bc) Lunar and Planetary Institute, 138(cl) JUAN CARLOS CASADO (starryearth.com)/SPL, 138(tl) Thomas Pajot/S, 138(tr) Thomas Bethge/S, 138(tr) JOE TUCCIARONE/SPL, 139(br) NASA, 139(cl) Boston Globe/Contributor/GI, 139(cl) Thomas Pajot/S, 139(tl) Thomas Bethge/S, 139(tl) HRIS BUTLER/SPL, 140–1 DETLEV VAN RAVENSWAAY/SPL, 140–1(bg) Michal Modzelewski/S, 140(b) NASA/JPL-Caltech/Malin Space Sci/Kinetikon Pictures/CO, 140(tr) Seamartini Graphics/S, 141(b) DETLEV VAN RAVENSWAAY/SPL, 141(br) iurii/S, 141(cr) NASA/SPL, 141(tl) GIL BABIN/LOOK AT SCIENCES/SPL, 142 NASA/JPL, 142–3 SCIEPRO/SPL, 142–3(bg) nikkytok/S, 143(b) CALIFORNIA ASSOCIATION FOR RESEARCH IN ASTRONOMY/SPL, 143(tr) NASA/JPL, 144–5(bg) kzww/S, 144(t) Megin/S, 144(tr) Nattika/S, 145(bl) US GEOLOGICAL SURVEY/SPL, 145(br) NASA/JPL/Ted Stryk, 145(cl) NASA/SPL, 145(cr) NASA/SPL, 145(tl) NASA/JPL/UNIVERSITY OF ARIZONA/SPL, 145(tr) NASA/SPL, 146–7(bg) Procy/S, 146(cl) Paper Street Design/S, 146(cl) DETLEV VAN RAVENSWAAY/SPL, 147(bl) Princeton University, 147(br) CHRIS BUTLER/SPL, 147(tl) AFP PHOTO/ SINC/ JOSE ANTONIO PENAS, 147(tr) CALIFORNIA ASSOCIATION FOR RESEARCH IN ASTRONOMY/SPL, 148–9(bg) Procy/S, 148(b) NASA/ESA/STSCI/J.CLARKE, BOSTON U./SPL, 148(bl) jannoon028/S, 148(t) NASA/SPL, 149(r) EUROPEAN SPACE AGENCY/SPL, 149(tl) RF

150 Vasily Smirnov/S

All other photographs are from: Corel, digitalSTOCK, digitalvision, Dreamstime.com, Fotolia.com, iStockphoto.com, John Foxx, PhotoAlto, PhotoDisc, PhotoEssentials, PhotoPro, Stockbyte

Every effort has been made to acknowledge the source and copyright holder of each picture. The publishers apologize for any unintentional errors or omissions.